Ketocooking

A practical guide to the ketogenic diet

Ketocooking

A practical guide to the ketogenic diet

Judy Nation • J Helen Cross • Ingrid E Scheffer

THE HOMEWOOD PRESS

Important

This book and the recipes in it should only be used when a child is being seen in an established, medically supervised ketogenic diet program, and the child is being regularly reviewed by a ketogenic diet team.

A ketogenic diet team usually includes a paediatric neurologist, paediatric epilepsy nurse and an experienced paediatric dietitian. The recipes have been designed for use in conjunction with a ketogenic diet calculator or manual calculation. Please make sure that your ketogenic diet team is consulted for assistance in using these recipes if you are just starting the diet.

In this book, we endeavour to cover medical issues of concern to families using the ketogenic diet. Although we have given simple management guidelines, if your child is unwell or you are worried, you should contact your ketogenic diet team. The book has been designed to give an outline of management, not act in place of medical review should it be necessary.

Never attempt to use this diet without strict medical supervision.

First published in 2012 by
The Homewood Press, 2 Chene Mews, St Albans, Hertfordshire, AL3 5QF

Text copyright © Judy Nation, J Helen Cross and Ingrid E Scheffer
Design and layout copyright © The Homewood Press
Photography © Greg Elms Photography

The authors' moral rights have been asserted.

ISBN: 978-0-9572787-0-7

10 9 8 7 6 5 4 3 2 1

Printed in China by Everbest Printing Co. Ltd.
Project manager: Joanna Copestick Design: Vanessa Courtier

Contents

Introduction

Since becoming patron of Matthew's Friends in 2005 I have seen the charity grow enormously helping hundreds of children and adults suffering with epilepsy through the ketogenic diet.

Children especially often have very fixed ideas about what they like and dislike when it comes to food which can be tricky when they are having to follow a strict diet. Sometimes all it takes is for food to be presented to them in a different way to get them to try new tastes.

This book aims to guide you through the recipes, all of which have been tried and tested by friends already using the diet and help you adapt dishes to encourage your children to experiment with new food.

Our aim is to make life a bit easier for you and to give you inspiration as you embark on your ketogenic journey. I hope you not only enjoy cooking the recipes but most importantly that your children enjoy eating them!

Happy "Ketocooking!"

Best wishes

Tony Tobin

Welcome to the ketogenic diet cookbook

The ketogenic diet has helped to make life better for many children with epilepsy. Due to the tireless cooking and preparation of the diet by mothers, fathers and carers, many children with epilepsy have experienced an improved quality of life as a result of the diet.

We have written this book because there are few resources of its kind available. We have combined practical information on management of the diet with recipes for meal and snack preparation. The introductory section aims to answer the most frequently asked questions that parents, carers and health professionals have about the diet. Many of the recipes have been contributed by parents wanting to make tasty, easy to prepare meals for their children.

We thank these amazing families for their contributions and hope you find their hints and suggestions as useful as they have. Whether it is a main meal or a snack, we are sure you will find something to suit your child's food preferences and your culinary skills.

Happy cooking and exploring!

Judy Nation
J Helen Cross
Ingrid E Scheffer

What is a ketogenic diet?

A ketogenic diet is a calculated, medically managed diet which requires careful planning to initiate. Regular monitoring under the supervision of an experienced ketogenic diet team is necessary to ensure its correct implementation and identify side effects. The diet controls seizures by changing the body's primary metabolism from carbohydrate to fat as the main energy source. This book aims to provide information so that parents or carers of children on the diet feel comfortable with its day to day management.

The diet is a non-drug dietary therapy available as a treatment option for children with epilepsy. It is usually suggested when children have seizures which are not responsive to conventional anti-epileptic drug therapy, or children suffer significant side effects from their medications.

It was first used as a treatment option for epilepsy in the 1920's and widely used until the 1950's, when it fell from favour due to the development of anti-epileptic medications. Over recent years, interest in use of the ketogenic diet has again increased.

The diet appears to be equally effective in all parts of the world. Ten percent of children will become seizure free and up to 50% will have a very good response. One third of children do not respond to the diet. Anectodal reports suggest an improvement in alertness and behaviour but this has not been proven scientifically. It should be remembered that the ketogenic diet is not appropriate for all children with epilepsy and in some cases it is contraindicated. Whether or not the diet is suitable for your child should be assessed by your doctor.

Types of ketogenic diets

The Classical ketogenic diet

The Classical ketogenic diet, developed by Johns Hopkins University, Baltimore, USA, is the most widely used type of ketogenic diet. It frequently uses 4 grams of long chain fat to every 1 gram of carbohydrate and protein combined. This is described as a 4:1 ratio and means 90% of total energy is provided from long chain fat. The remaining energy in the Classical ketogenic diet is provided as below:

1 5-7% of the total energy as protein
2 3-5% of the total energy as carbohydrate

For a child, the amount of energy needed in the Classical ketogenic diet is generally estimated by consideration of the following:

1 Current dietary intake
2 Current weight and height
3 85% of Recommended Dietary Intake (RDI) for energy for age
4 Growth history and desirable growth
5 Activity level

The total energy prescription for a child on the Classical ketogenic diet should allow for normal growth and development while maintaining the desired level of ketosis. Excessive calories may result in unnecessary weight gain, while too few calories may lead to poor growth; both situations can compromise ketosis and the effectiveness of the diet. For this reason, the initial ketogenic diet plan needs to be regularly monitored and adjusted, especially during the first few months of treatment. Sufficient protein is required to allow for normal growth and development. It should therefore meet the recommended daily intake for ideal body weight and normal growth.

The initial diet ratio is usually set between a 3:1-4:1 ratio, and is partly determined by the child's protein needs. Infants and very young children require more protein per kg of body weight than older children. Due to the rapid growth experienced in puberty, adolescents also have a higher requirement for protein. Both situations usually necessitate a ratio lower than 4:1; a 3:1 ratio is generally used.

The Medium Chain Triglyceride (MCT) Diet

A modification of the Classical ketogenic diet was introduced in the 1970's using Medium Chain Triglyceride (MCT) as an alternative fat source. MCT fats, octanoic and decanoic acid, have a higher ketone yield per unit of energy than their long-chain fat counterparts. This increased ketogenic potential means that less fat is required in the diet, and therefore allows more protein and carbohydrate to be included. Thus the MCT diet may significantly improve the taste and palatability of the ketogenic diet. Although there have been some concerns that the MCT ketogenic diet may be less successful in treating seizures due to its more relaxed protocol, a recent study found that the two types of diet were equally effective.

The MCT ketogenic diet allows for up to 60% of the fat to be given as MCT but the exact percentage should be tailored to each child's requirements. The MCT fat is given in the form of an oil or emulsion, and the long chain fats as butter or cream. Usually the MCT fat level starts at around 40-50% of total energy to minimize abdominal problems, such as pain and diarrhoea, and to achieve good levels of ketosis. The remaining energy in the MCT ketogenic diet is provided overleaf:

1   10-12% of the total energy as protein
2   15-19% of the total energy as carbohydrate
3   The remaining energy from long-chain fat in food

Many centres which employ the MCT ketogenic diet version use food "exchanges" to design meals. A child will be given a ketogenic diet prescription based on a set number of "exchanges" for fat, protein and carbohydrate per meal. From exchange lists carers are able to select food portions to design meals.

MCT fat should be included in all meals and snacks and is provided from MCT oil or MCT emulsions (Liquigen®). Some centres use "exchanges" of equivalent food compositions as part of this diet.

A few words about food

The energy-providing nutrient components of food are carbohydrate, protein and fat predominantly in the form of long chain triglycerides (LCT). Approximately 30-40% of total energy in the Western child's diet is derived from LCT fat. More than half of their energy is derived from carbohydrate (also called sugar). On the Classical ketogenic diet, a child consumes approximately 90% of their total energy as LCT fat, predominantly provided by oil, butter, margarine, cream and mayonnaise. On an MCT ketogenic diet, a child consumes 40-50% of their total energy as MCT fat and approximately 25-35% of their total energy as LCT fat.

On the Classical ketogenic diet, carbohydrate and protein foods provide the remaining 10% of energy and are limited. "Carbohydrate" foods include bread, cereals, pasta, rice, potatoes and corn (most people know these as starches), milk and yoghurt (lactose), fruits (fructose), vegetables, lollies and sweet drinks (sucrose). "Protein" foods include meat, chicken, fish, cheese and eggs. There is still enough protein in the diet to allow your child to grow.

Fat yields more energy per gram than protein and carbohydrate. One gram of fat provides 9 kilocalories (a unit of energy) compared with 1 gram of protein or carbohydrate; each provides 4 kilocalories. Because of this, meals look much smaller than usual and you may worry that your child should feel hungry. This should not happen if caloric intake is correctly calculated. If your child is hungry, and they are not gaining weight appropriately, then the total energy in the ketogenic diet may require adjustment.

A history of this resource

Over the past few years, recognition of the benefits of the ketogenic diet has increased, and consequently there has been a greater demand for its use. More and more families are looking for ways of reducing seizure activity in their child when medication has not worked or where surgery is not possible. There are also medical indications for the use of the diet in children who have specific metabolic problems which are more widely applicable in epilepsy than previously thought. In addition, families are keen to play a major role in helping their child.

Demand for the ketogenic diet is increasing and children are staying on it for longer. On starting the diet, parents often ask "What am I going to feed my child that is tasty and easy to prepare?" Later, parents ask "What can I give my child for variety?" Answers to these questions are difficult to find in a book format. Over time it became obvious that the people who could help answer the "foodie" questions were the families of children already on the diet. We wanted every family, including those beginning or already on the diet, to have ready access to this information in the kitchen.

Notes about using this book and recipe modification

Although the basic principles are the same, every child's ketogenic diet "prescription" is unique. The combination of total energy, protein, fat and carbohydrate, and the dietary ratio will differ from child to child as no two children will have a nutritional requirement that is exactly the same.

As the recipes in this book have been standardized, it is unlikely that they will meet the exact nutritional requirements of your child and these will need to be modified according to your child's exact prescription. This is not hard to do, it may just take a little practice.

How to use
the recipes

Classical ketogenic diet For each recipe, three dietary options are given in different ratios of 3:1, 3.5:1 and 4:1. Precise ingredient amounts in grams are given for each ingredient according to these ratios for every recipe. The amount of energy and protein provided for each ratio is shown at the bottom of the table. The recipes should be used as a guide for the relative ingredient amounts required, however, the actual amounts need to be calculated according to your child's dietary prescription. This can either be done using a ketogenic calculator (see appendices) or by manual calculation with the help of your ketogenic dietitian. An example of how to manipulate a recipe so that it meets a specific dietary prescription is given overleaf:

Example: Chicken Stir Fry (see p56)

Your child's prescription is: 7.3g protein, 420 kcal; 4:1 ratio

step 1   Enter your child's dietary prescription into the ketogenic calculator

step 2   Enter chicken stir fry values from chicken stir fry recipe (4:1 ratio) into
a ketogenic calculator

step 3   Decrease carbohydrate intake while maintaining bulk from vegetables:
suggest: decrease carrot to 16g, add cabbage 16g
and decrease onion to 8g
and decrease capsicum to 22g

step 4   Increase protein intake:
suggest: increase chicken to 25g

step 5   Decrease fat intake
suggest: decrease rice bran oil to 41g

New recipe:

Ingredient:	4:1 amount
red capsicum	22g
carrot, peeled	16g
cabbage	16g
onion	8g
green beans	33g
rice bran oil	41g
chicken breast	25g

makes 1 serve providing
418kcal, 7.4g protein

This recipe will combine well as there are plenty of vegetables and chicken to absorb the oil. It is really important to think about the amounts of ingredients being used. Will your ingredients, in the amounts you have allocated, combine well?

An example of a recipe modification that would NOT work is given below:

Banana and Coconut Muffins (see p102)

Your child's prescription is: 4g protein, 250kcal; 4:1 ratio

step 1   Enter your child's dietary prescription into the ketogenic calculator (remember to multiply this prescription by 4 as the recipe you are adjusting makes 4 muffins; you would therefore enter 1000kcal, 16g protein and a 4:1 ratio)

step 2   Enter banana and coconut muffin values from banana and coconut muffin recipe (4:1 ratio) into a ketogenic calculator

step 3   Decrease carbohydrate intake
          suggest: decrease banana to 16g

step 4   Increase protein intake:
          suggest: increase whole egg to 79g

step 5   Decrease carbohydrate intake again
          suggest: decrease banana to 14g

step 6   Increase fat intake
          suggest: increase oil intake to 34g

New recipe:

Ingredient:	4:1 amount
banana, mashed	14g
whole egg, beaten	79g
double thick cream (55% fat)	30g
rice bran oil	34g
almond meal	10g
macadamia nuts, ground to meal	15g
desiccated coconut	25g
butter, softened	10g
self raising flour	3g
ground cinnamon	½ teaspoon
liquid artificial sweetener (optional)	to taste

makes 4 muffins
each providing
250kcal, 4g protein

This recipe would not work well because the ingredients which provide moisture to the muffins: banana, egg and oil, have almost doubled in quantity. This muffin mixture would be too greasy and not bake properly.

It is difficult to manipulate this recipe to suit this particular dietary prescription; increasing the protein component will automatically decrease the ratio and so extra fat will be needed. This results in a more liquid mixture that is not desirable for baking.

One suggestion is to consume a ketogenic supplement alongside the muffin. Ketocal®
works very well in this situation.

New recipe:

Ingredient:	4:1 amount
banana, mashed	33g
whole egg, beaten	15g
double thick cream (55% fat)	30g
rice bran oil	23g
almond meal	10g
macadamia nuts, ground to meal	15g
desiccated coconut	25g
butter, softened	10g
self raising flour	3g
ground cinnamon	½ teaspoon
liquid artificial sweetener (optional)	to taste
additional supplement	
Ketocal®	102g
water	approximately 500ml
	makes 6 serves each providing 262kcal, 4g protein

In this example the muffin mixture is divided into 6 equal portions. Each muffin is then consumed with a Ketocal® drink (made from Ketocal® (17g) mixed with water (85ml)). If you prefer, you can make the muffins with Ketocal® instead of having it as a drink on the side. The mixture comes out like a "dough" for biscuits. If you prefer to keep them as muffins then add some extra water.

Ingredient type

When buying food products for the recipes in this book it is important to check that the nutrient values of the food product (per 100g) are the same as the values in your ketogenic calculator.

Manufacturers make subtle changes to their food products regularly, so checking the label and updating your product list needs to occur whenever you buy a product.

We have not used specific brand names in the ingredient lists as product availability differs from region to region. For foods which may have varying nutrient profiles however, we have indicated the percentage protein, fat or carbohydrate.

A ketogenic diet shopping list can be found on p30.

Here are a few general tips for using these recipes:

1 Read through the recipe first to get an overview of what is involved. Have you got the necessary equipment? Do you have the correct ingredients?
2 Can the meal be made in large quantities so that you can keep portions for later use? Try to gauge this by the nature of the recipe. For example, a single consistency recipe such as strawberry mousse is well suited to be made in large quantities. When a single consistency recipe is portioned, each serve has the same dietary ratio although the energy amount may vary slightly with the serving size. Meals which consist of large amounts of individual ingredients do not work well, for example, chicken stir fry. It is difficult to ensure that the exact amount of chicken in each portioned serve is equivalent, and so the correct dietary ratio of each serve cannot be guaranteed. A meal such as this could still be prepared ahead of time however; individual ingredients can be weighed and frozen, then defrosted and prepared as required.

Thinking about the diet

When is the diet indicated?

The ketogenic diet can effectively treat epilepsy in individuals of all ages although it has largely been used in children. Until recently the ketogenic diet was reserved for those who did not respond to multiple anti-epileptic medications. Nowadays the ketogenic diet is being considered earlier.

The ketogenic diet has been used for children with any type of epilepsy but particular success has been described in the syndromes of epilepsy with myoclonic-atonic seizures (Doose syndrome), tuberous sclerosis, Rett syndrome, Dravet syndrome, and infantile spasms.

The ketogenic diet is the treatment of choice for the metabolic disorder glucose transporter 1 deficiency syndrome. Long term use of modified versions of the diet may also be of benefit in another metabolic disorder; pyruvate dehydrogenase deficiency.

When is the diet contraindicated?

The ketogenic diet is contraindicated in pyruvate carboxylase deficiency and organic acidurias because of the risk of low blood sugar.

How is the diet started?

1 Education and counselling
2 Nutritional and feeding evaluation performed by a specialist dietitian and epilepsy nurse specialist
3 Medical evaluation
4 Laboratory and ancillary investigations
5 Family and psychosocial dynamics

It is now widely accepted that hospital admission and fasting are not required to establish the diet. For young infants, admission is usual to monitor for low blood sugar and acidosis. Each centre will have their own protocol for initiation of the diet.

Who will help me manage the diet?

Initially your ketogenic diet team will provide you with a lot of information about how to prepare meals and manage the diet. You should feel free to ask them as many questions as you like. Other resources that you can access include parent support networks and relevant websites (see Resources p140).

As you become skilled in using the diet, you will need to educate those who help to look after your child including other family members, carers and teachers. This will ensure that your child is supported with the diet and may be left safely with other carers without compromising the diet.

Ultimately whoever is responsible for preparation of food must manage the diet and be organized.

Potential side effects

The ketogenic diet may have side effects, as can any treatment. The overall risk of side effects is low and most settle with changes to the diet. Your ketogenic diet team will monitor for side effects by recognising abnormalities in your child's blood biochemistry, growth and other dietary investigation results. Some changes are expected; these show that the diet is changing the body's metabolism appropriately, such as showing an acidosis on blood chemistry.

Possible side effects may include:

• Gastrointestinal symptoms: vomiting, constipation, diarrhoea, abdominal pain. These can generally be managed by manipulation of the diet.

• Abnormalities of minerals: calcium, magnesium, selenium, zinc. Mineral deficiency requires monitoring and supplementation in some children by the ketogenic diet team.

• High blood fats (hyperlipidaemia) including high blood cholesterol and, on the Classical diet only, high triglyceride levels in the blood. The exact long term effects are unclear.

• Renal stones occur in 5-8% of children on the diet. The risk is increased in younger children and those less mobile. Theoretically the risk may be increased if the child is also on medications such as topiramate, acetazolamide and zonisamide that also have a risk of renal stones.

• Growth may be slowed on the diet. Younger children are particularly at risk. This should be closely monitored by your ketogenic diet team.

• Vitamin D deficiency is increasingly recognized in children. Supplementation should be considered if levels are below 75nmol/L.

• Bone health problems may occur with vitamin D deficiency and low calcium. There may be a higher risk of fractures with long term use of the ketogenic diet. Anti-epileptic medications may also contribute to these side effects.

• Carnitine deficiency is a risk as requirements may increase when following a very high fat diet. Carnitine is involved in the transport of LCT into the cell for energy production. Children should be considered for supplementation if they are found to be deficient.

After the diet has started

How is the diet monitored?

The aim of the diet is for your child to achieve a high level of ketosis. You monitor this by measuring urinary ketone levels with ketone sticks. Initially this should be done twice per day until consistent ketone levels are established. At this point ketone levels may be monitored twice per week. At times of inadequate ketosis, blood ketone levels may be more indicative of the level of ketosis. Despite a high dietary ratio, urinary ketone levels may sometimes not be detectable. In some centres, blood ketone monitoring is preferred.

Your child will be required to attend regular outpatient visits for review with the ketogenic diet team. Your child will also need to have regular blood tests and other medical investigations. At the clinic visit, the team will ask you about your child's ketone levels, seizure frequency, tolerance of the diet, and overall well being. They will also obtain growth details and review test results. If there are concerns regarding any aspects of your child's health, you will be given the opportunity to discuss this with the team. It is rare for a child to have to discontinue the diet because of adverse side effects.

Medication and supplements

As with any new anti-epileptic medication the diet should be added to the existing drug regime. If the diet is effective over a period of time, then consideration can be given to reducing medication after discussion with your doctor. There are patients in whom drugs can be discontinued following an excellent response to the diet.

It is essential that medication is sugar-free so that the exact formulation of each medication may need to be changed to a sugar-free formulation. For example, a syrup may need to be changed to a sugar-free liquid or crushable tablets. This applies to all medication including pain relief and antibiotics.

At the present time, there are no medications that are absolutely contraindicated with the ketogenic diet although some medications may require increased monitoring. For example, with topiramate or zonisamide, renal ultrasound prior to the initiation of the diet is considered to ensure that there are no kidney stones prior to starting the diet. Valproate may give a false positive ketone reading in the urine and this also needs consideration. In some centres, children at higher risk of kidney stones may be started on potassium citrate to lessen the risk.

Carbohydrate-free vitamin and mineral supplementation is essential due to the restriction of the ketogenic diet to ensure that they receive their daily recommended intake. Regular blood tests are necessary to ensure that your child is given the correct amount.

Is the diet working?

The diet can take up to three months to show benefit but improvement may be evident within a few weeks. It may take some adjustment to achieve the appropriate level of ketosis. During this time, the ketogenic diet team can establish if there has been a favourable response and if the family are coping with the diet. For most children, the decision to continue the diet is based on the degree of improvement in their seizures as well as their overall well being. The decision needs to be made by the child, their family and the ketogenic diet team.

Excessive ketosis

If ketosis occurs rapidly, sometimes the child may become vague, lethargic and flushed. This can also occur if ketones become too high once the child is established on the diet. The question of what ketone level defines "excessive ketosis" is not well established. For some children, serum ketones above 5 mmol/L will be associated with symptoms, whereas other children tolerate such levels without ill effect.

Symptoms of high ketones include:

- the child is less responsive than usual

- unusual tiredness

- loss of appetite

- nausea and vomiting

- excessive "fruity" odour on the breath (fruity odour is usual on the diet)

- irritability

- facial flushing

- very rapid, panting breathing or shortness of breath.

This state can be confirmed by testing with a urine ketone stick which will rapidly turn black.

Special situations

Kindergarten, crèche and school considerations

Leaving your child in the hands of another carer for meals can be stressful. Stress can be minimized if the following questions are considered in advance of leaving your child in planned care:

1 Does the centre's food policy allow food to be brought from home? Are the staff happy to reheat food brought from home on the premises?

2 What level of supervision are the staff able to offer for your child while they are eating? Could your child accidentally receive non-ketogenic diet food while in the centre's care, such as from another child or staff member?

3 Do you feel confident your child will eat the meal provided for them?

4 What should the staff do if your child refuses to eat?

Restaurants

Eating out as a family in many restaurants can be a daunting prospect if your child is on a ketogenic diet.

Options:

1 Some restaurants may allow you to bring your child's meal and have them reheat it, particularly if they know you. Check before you go to avoid disappointment; if they do not allow the reheating of food it is likely due to the health and safety regulations which they must follow.

2 Choose menu items which are plain foods and take your own scales. Telephone the restaurant before you go and see what choices of food they do offer. Ask for copies of the menus at eateries you plan to eat at often. If your child is taking supplements with their meals, for example; Ketocal® or Liquigen®, do not forget to take these with you. It is also wise to take those foods with you which are brand specific such as mayonnaises and sauces. Their nutritional composition can vary greatly and so potentially affect ketone levels and seizure control.

Birthday parties

You and your child both want to have as regular a life as possible, so birthday parties, picnics and other social events should be attended as much as possible. Being organized for the occasion means that your child can attend and enjoy themselves. It is unlikely the food provided will cater for your child's needs so consider the following beforehand:

1 Check that the party organizer is happy if you bring your child's own food. If the other children are all having their food in party boxes, ask for one to put your child's ketogenic diet food in so that they can be the same.

2 Somebody will need to ensure your child has their specific food and nothing else, so you may need to arrange for someone to supervise, if not you personally.

3 When they are old enough, educate your child on the importance of their ketogenic diet food. Involve them in food preparation so that they learn to recognize those foods they are allowed and those they are not allowed, and the portion sizes of foods which they can eat.

Travelling

Planning and organization are the keys to successful travel. If you plan to travel for longer than a week, or to a foreign country, it is recommended that you discuss this with your ketogenic diet team in advance. They should be able to guide you to information on the following:

1 Food and food values for the area in which you are travelling.

2 Protocols to manage illness while you are away.

3 Alternative food suggestions if basic ingredients are unavailable.

The following would be useful to travel with:

1 A letter including your child's details, diagnosis, management of the condition and their ketogenic diet. This can be provided by your ketogenic diet team who can emphasize the importance of the diet for your child's medical care.

2 A letter of cover for any extra foods that you might need to take eg. MCT oil, Ketocal®, Liquigen®.

3 Scales and urine or blood testing devices (with letter of cover if required).

4 Your computer program (ie EKM) for recipe/meal manipulation.

5 Protocol for illness management.

6 Estimation of dietary requirements for journey.

7 Ketogenic diet team contact details at destination.

Considerations before travelling

1 Contact the airline to ensure that they will let you take your child's food with you. Determine ahead if they will provide appropriate refrigeration. Do not assume that they will provide suitable foods.

2 Remember the journey time includes to and from the airport and to your accommodation. Ensure you have sufficient provisions in case of delay in your travels. Having an all in one meal, such as a muffin, can be really useful in the event of delay.

3 Organize to provide ketogenic diet meals once you arrive at your destination. You will need to check what cooking and refrigerator facilities are available when you arrive. You may need to immediately buy and prepare ketogenic diet food.

Fluid

It is very important to maintain an adequate fluid intake, particularly if going somewhere warm. Travelling on aeroplanes also increases the requirement for fluid and so regular fluid intake is very important.

Time-zones and eating

Aim for ketogenic meals and snacks to be consumed at approximately the same intervals they would be if you were not travelling. This means that your child will consume adequate fat and energy and so their usual level of ketosis should be maintained. It is not a problem if your child eats a little more over a 24-hour period. You should switch to the normal meal times for your new time zone when you arrive to establish a routine.

Portable food ideas

Children often prefer simple plain foods:

- Frittata/omelette
- Quiche
- Muffins/cake/cookies
- Salads - cheese, vegetables and lettuce leaves plus mayonnaise, dip or oil.

- Kebabs with dip, mayonnaise or oil
- Vegetables with dip, mayonnaise or oil
- Pizza - experiment with different toppings
- Sausage rolls
- Desserts - cream, nuts, strawberries, unsweetened chocolate, fruit

Although these foods travel well, it may be necessary to transport them in an insulated cool-box. This will depend on the type of food and the length of time they will be non-refrigerated.

If you are in a situation where you do not have enough food, many fast food restaurants provide nutritional information on the foods they sell. It is often possible for your child to eat their food if this nutritional information is known and calculated into their diet.

Help! My child won't eat!

Every parent worries when their child will not eat because it can affect their usual level of ketosis. Ketone levels tend to drop when a child is not eating or eating much less than normal.

Lowered ketone levels occur for two main reasons:

1 The child is consuming less food and so less fat is available to convert into ketones.

2 The child enters a "fasting state" and so has less energy. They will use their fat stores, however, these stores are not as readily available, and thus the child will become less ketotic.

Even if the child is well controlled on the diet, a small change in ketosis may affect their seizure control.

Parents sometimes attribute the reason that their child is not eating to dislike of the ketogenic diet. This is rarely the case. A child on a ketogenic diet usually rejects food for the same reasons as a child on a regular diet. They may not like the food being offered, they may lose their appetite either due to being full or nauseated, or perhaps a behavioural element, such as attention seeking, is playing a part. It should be emphasized that serving portions are smaller and parents may perceive that their child is not receiving enough nutrition when in fact the diet is adequately balanced.

Some basic strategies to help your child eat at meal times:

- Reinforce normal eating behaviours at mealtimes; prepare your child for a meal in advance, offer meals in a relaxed environment, eliminate distractions, turn off the television.

• Adhere to the usual routine. If a child refuses a meal or snack, then they should wait until their next meal or snack before more food is offered.

• Meals and snacks should be eaten with other family members where possible to enable the important social interaction that occurs around a meal table.

• Meal times should take no longer that 30 minutes, snack times should take no longer than 15 minutes.

• Praise the child when they eat all of their meal.

• A key to success is allowing some degree of choice for the child so that they eat what they enjoy. If the child has only a few meals that they like, these can be rotated and gradually other foods can be introduced once they are established on the diet.

Remember ketosis will be re-established when your child starts eating again or starts to eat more. If your child refuses to eat and they are not maintaining their usual fluid intake, then they are at risk of becoming dehydrated. Signs of dehydration include dry lips and mouth, fewer wet nappies, drowsiness as well as cold hands and feet. Management of dehydration can be found in the section: Illness (see p26).

Help! My child won't drink!

It is very important that your child gets enough fluid when they are on a ketogenic diet because of the risk of dehydration. Sometimes it can be challenging. Your child may be missing their favourite drinks such as non-diet soft drinks, milk, fruit juices, and cordial. Signs that your child may not be getting enough fluid include a decrease in the number of wet nappies (and so it may be very difficult to measure urine ketone levels), dry mouth, sunken eyes and tiredness. Ask your ketogenic diet team to estimate how much fluid your child needs each day.

Ideas to help increase your child's fluid intake when they are on the ketogenic diet are:

1 Water can be made more interesting by:
    a Adding 20ml diet lemonade to every 200ml of water
    b Adding 1-2 teaspoons of fresh lemon juice and 1-2 drops of liquid artificial sweetener to every 200ml water to make lemonade
    c Pure vanilla essence can also be added.

2 Freeze (a) and (b) in ice-block moulds to make ice-pops/icypoles.

3 Ice-pops/icypoles can also be made by freezing cream, diet lemonade and water.

4 Make a milkshake from cream, water, artificial sweetener, fruit (as part of carbohydrate allowance or "free" strawberry allowance) and pure flavoured extracts. The amount of each ingredient will depend on your child's individual ketogenic diet prescription.

5 Make a jelly using sugar free jelly crystals, water, double thick cream and pure flavoured extracts.

6 Offer drinks in brightly coloured cups and use colourful straws.

7 If possible, add a little extra water to cooked dishes.

8 In the cooler months encourage soups made from plenty of vegetables and water.

Illness

Every parent worries when their child becomes unwell. When a child is on a ketogenic diet it can be particularly worrying as it can affect their level of ketosis. Ketone levels may increase or decrease with illness. If they decrease, your child may be at risk of increased seizures.

Very high
ketone levels

On the ketogenic diet, children generally tolerate high ketone levels. Sometimes these levels may however become too high. This is usually caused by:

• the ketogenic diet ratio being too high
• the child being unwell such as with gastroenteritis

If the ketone levels are too high your child may have some or all of the symptoms of excessive ketosis (see p20).

When your child's ketone levels are very high, their blood sugar levels are usually very low. Treatment for excessive ketosis therefore involves giving your child some extra carbohydrate. A prescribed dose of a carbohydrate containing liquid, such as orange juice or regular lemonade, is generally ideal if ketone levels are too high. Both are easy for a child to take and readily absorbed as long as the child is well enough to drink. The amount can be repeated if there has been no sign of improvement. Always contact your ketogenic diet team in this situation and alert them that your child is unwell.

Hydration

It is very common for unwell children to eat and drink less than usual. This may be due to a number of reasons:

- they feel nauseated
- they are unusually tired and sleeping a lot
- they are vomiting
- they have diarrhoea
- they have very high ketone levels and may not be drinking due to symptoms of excessive ketosis (see p20)

If your child is unable to maintain their usual intake, they are at risk of becoming dehydrated (see p25).

Management of dehydration

If they are able to drink, the following fluids can be used:

- Water
- Repalyte® and Diarolyte® which are oral rehydration solutions, and should be made up as per the directions on the packet
- Hydralyte® is another oral rehydration solution that is available as ice-blocks or powder

Your doctor will give you guidelines to establish how much fluid your child should be drinking. If you are concerned, then your child should be seen by your doctor.

Once your child is rehydrated, it is important to continue with sugar free liquids or oral rehydration solutions to prevent recurrence of dehydration. Ketogenic diet meals can usually be recommended once you feel that your child can tolerate them.

When to contact the hospital

In some situations, your child may need to be assessed at the hospital. You should seek the support of your ketogenic diet team at the hospital if:

- your child is vomiting and/or has diarrhoea; and does not want to drink or is not keeping down any fluids.
- your child is excessively ketotic, particularly if several doses of a carbohydrate containing fluid have been administered and their condition has not improved.

To manage dehydration it may be necessary for the doctor to give some fluid via a feeding tube or directly into a vein. If supportive intravenous fluids are required, remember to tell the doctor that your child is on the ketogenic diet so that the appropriate fluid is administered. In many cases, this will be half normal saline (0.45% NaCl). Some ketogenic diet teams provide a letter outlining an emergency protocol for such situations.

These guidelines are by no means complete and do not substitute for the advice that your ketogenic diet team will give you at times when your child is unwell.

Tips and tricks

Useful kitchen utensils (highly recommended)

The following is a list, which is by no means comprehensive, of some of the recommended kitchen utensils you could have:

1 1g increment scales.

2 Soft plastic spatulas of different sizes are used for scraping all oil and cream from beaters, bowls, etc.

3 Teabag squeezers for handling small foods.

4 Sharp knife which enables thinner slices of food to allow more fat to be absorbed.

5 Ramekins of mixed sizes (eg 6-8cm and 10cm) are useful for jellies, cheesecakes, and mini casseroles.

6 Several non-stick frying pans of different sizes.

7 Sealable plastic bowls (or small durable freezer bags) for food storage when cooking in bulk. Ensure they are microwave and freezer proof (eg. GLAD® Micro & Freezing).

8 V-slicer to allow foods to be sliced or grated paper thin and absorb more fat.

9 Small food processor or hand mixer which can be used for blending or pureeing foods to make soups, smoothies. This will ensure a consistent dietary ratio.

10 Several Esky/coolbox packs for travel and school.

Cook in bulk and give yourself a break!

When you discover a meal that your child enjoys, you can save time by pre-preparing many servings at once. Not only does bulk cooking save time but it may allow you to feel more comfortable leaving your child in someone else's care at mealtimes. Meals can be pre-prepared in bulk, either fully-cooked OR weighed into their raw ingredient components and stored in the refrigerator or freezer to be used when desired.

Method:

1 Cut/slice/grate all raw vegetables in bulk quantities (using a grater, "V-slicer" or food processor).

2 Place a storage container onto your scales prior to measuring the first ingredient. Reset the scale to zero and repeat this process with the same ingredient in each container in turn.

3 Using your next ingredient repeat step 2 until all of the raw vegetables are measured.

4 Label the container with the date and the contents eg. "vegetables in chicken stir fry".

5 Store containers in refrigerator or freezer.

6 Repeat the process above with the "protein" component of the meal (freezing of uncooked meats/chicken and vegetables together is not recommended because of the risk of infection).

7 When you are ready to prepare the meal, only thawing and adding the fat component is required.

8 Preparing meals such as quiche in bulk is also useful. As long as each ingredient is evenly spread across the mixture, then you can be assured that each portion will be in the correct ratio and therefore has the correct amount of energy. Grating vegetables and finely chopping meats and chicken ensures that this is the case.

NB Protein foods should not be frozen, thawed, and then refrozen as this increases the risk of food contamination. When using raw protein foods in meals, they should be weighed and added when they are first brought home from the supermarket or butcher.

Ketogenic diet shopping list

Shopping list

The following is a list of some of the foods and special food products which are useful when cooking ketogenic meals and snacks. Many of these foods have been used in the recipes which follow.

Main sources of fat

Oils:
Rice bran oil: This is inexpensive, and has a low boiling point, is flavourless and so can be used in large quantities; available from large supermarkets.

Olive, sesame, vegetable oils: These are derived from plant rather than animal fats; impart a variety of flavours.

Cooking spray: A cholesterol free canola or a rice bran oil spray is useful for greasing oven trays without the need for incorporation into the diet prescription.

Margarine:
Adds texture to cooking without the moisture of oil. Most contain some carbohydrate. However several carbohydrate free versions are available (see Australian Brands p138).

Butter:
Adds good flavour. Like margarine, it adds texture to cooking without excessive moisture. Unsalted butter is generally better for cakes and biscuits; whereas salted butter adds flavour to savoury meals. Contains some carbohydrate which needs to be incorporated into the dietary prescription. Is an animal fat (saturated) and so the amount incorporated into the diet may need modification.

Cream:
Thickened (~35% fat): This is the most common type of cream used. It is of a pouring consistency but can also be whipped to provide texture. A whipping cream containing thickener has at least 35% fat content.

Sour (~35% fat): Thick, commercially-cultured sour cream with at least 35% fat content can be used as an alternative to thickened cream to flavour meals and desserts.

Double thick (50-56% fat): An extremely thick cream with at least 48% fat content; useful in quiches, frittatas as it provides texture. It may be mixed with water to provide a ketogenic drink.

Clotted (>60% fat): This is an alternative to double thick cream when more fat is required. It has at least 60% butterfat; useful in savoury dishes when texture is required and delicious in desserts.

Coconut (>30% fat): This provides a good source of fat as well as flavour in curries and Asian meals.

Other sources of fat

Mayonnaise: Each product varies significantly in fat content. Some contain more than 80% fat. These may be useful with salad or incorporated into dips and sauces.

Nuts and seeds: These can be eaten whole as part of a snack, or incorporated into main meals or salads. They are useful in baked products such as muffins. They can be ground into meal such as almond meal and hazelnut meal.

Almond: A brown husk within a green outer coating. Frequently ground to a coarse flour texture to make almond meal.

Pistachio: A green, delicately flavoured nut in a hard, off-white shell. Available salted or unsalted.

Brazil: A triangular-shelled oily nut with tender white flesh and a mild flavour.

Pecan: A golden brown, buttery, rich nut.

Macadamia: A rich, buttery nut. Has a very high oil content so should be stored in the refrigerator. May be blended to make a spread similar to peanut butter.

Sesame: Small, dried, yellow-brown seeds; soft and chewy. Available from supermarkets. Tahini is a paste made from sesame seeds which is very low in carbohydrate and high in fat. May be used as a dressing for raw or cooked vegetables.

Hazelnut: A small round nut with a pointed tip in a brown skin. It may be ground to a coarse flour texture to make hazelnut meal. Also blended to make a spread similar to peanut butter.

Pine nut: Softer than most other nuts and has an oily, slightly mealy texture. Because of these properties, it is ideally blended to a paste: pesto.

Peanut: Not a true nut but a pod of a leguminous plant. Used to make peanut butter; these vary in both fat and carbohydrate content.

Nut spreads: Hazelnut.

Seed pastes: Tahini.

Peanut butter: Products vary in fat and carbohydrate content. Some contain more than 50% fat and are lower in carbohydrate.

Cheeses: There is a large range to choose from with varying tastes and textures. They differ in protein and fat content. Most cheddars range between 30-35% fat and contain some carbohydrate. Some vintage cheddars provide about 37% total energy as fat. Some soft cheeses provide more than 40% total energy as fat.

Cheddar: Ranges between 30-35% fat content and contains some carbohydrate.

Vintage cheddars have approximately 37% fat content and are stronger in flavour than standard cheddars. They also have minimal carbohydrate.

Cream: Commonly called "Philadelphia" or "Philly", a soft cow milk cheese with fat content of at least 33%. Useful in making both savoury and sweet dishes.

Fetta: Greek in origin; a crumbly goat or sheep-milk cheese with a salty flavour.

Parmesan: A hard, grainy cows' milk cheese. Only small quantities needed due to its strong flavour.

Avocado: This is very useful in salads, incorporated into dips and used as a spread with vegetables.

Coconut: This is useful in salads. It can also be used as a garnish for main meals and sweets when extra fat is required.

Cream: Obtained commercially from the first pressing of the coconut flesh alone. Useful as a base for curries and asian style meals.

Desiccated: Dried, unsweetened and finely shredded coconut flesh. See Baking Products (p33).

Shredded: Unsweetened thin strips of dried coconut. Used to garnish both savoury and sweet dishes.

Main sources of protein

Meat: Includes beef, lamb, pork, veal, ham, bacon and others; can be eaten as fillets, chops or minced. These cuts cook quickly and so oil is absorbed into the meat, not onto the dish. Contain no carbohydrate, however differ in fat content; both lean and fatty varieties are available. The incorporation of leaner meats will ensure a better quality of protein. Products such as sausages and salami may also contain some carbohydrate.

Poultry: Chicken fillets and mince, turkey fillets, duck

Fish: Tuna, salmon, white fish

Eggs: Essential for quiche, frittata and as a binder in baking

Cheese: See previous page.

Main sources of carbohydrate	**Vegetables:** Carrot, zucchini (also called courgette), onion, red, green and yellow peppers/capsicum, bean sprouts, red and green cabbage, tomato, lettuce, green beans, pumpkin, fresh herbs, broccoli, celery, cucumber, asian greens, eggplant (also called aubergine), mushrooms, avocado and more.

Fruits: Strawberries, raspberries, blueberries, blackberries, watermelon, cantaloupe, honeydew melon, rhubarb.

Other fruits are included however due to their high carbohydrate content only minimal amounts are allowed. These include banana, apple, pear, pineapple, apricot, peach, nectarine and more!

Baking products	**Desiccated coconut:** This is extremely useful in baking, for example, in muffins and biscuits. Its texture provides bulk in recipes and is often used as a flour substitute. It is high in fat so its addition to recipes increases the ketogenic ratio.

Nut meals: Available in most supermarkets and health food stores. Nuts can be ground at home to make your own nut meal. This is a less expensive option and the carbohydrate content will be less than store-bought nut meal. Like desiccated coconut very useful in the preparation of ketogenic muffins and biscuits.

Cocoa powder: This can be used in baking such as in muffins, biscuits and cream based desserts, as well as a flavouring for drinks. Both unsweetened and sweetened forms are available; it will depend on your child's ketogenic diet prescription which is more appropriate.

Gelatin: Available in both powder and sheet form. Gelatin powder is used as a setting agent for desserts such as mousse. It is comprised almost solely of protein and so even very small amounts need to be counted in recipe calculations.

Currants/sultanas: These are very high in carbohydrate so can only be used in very small amounts. They give a naturally sweet taste to muffins or biscuits.

Pure essences: These can be used freely in baking and cooking. A wide range of flavours is available (vanilla, almond, coconut, lemon and more).

Miscellaneous

Dried herbs and spices: Added into meals in usual quantities; considered "free" in the diet and so do not need to be counted. Their use is encouraged as they add flavour without affecting the ketogenic diet ratio.

Sauces: Low carbohydrate versions of commonly used sauces can be used to add flavour, such as tomato sauce. Even though these versions contain reduced carbohydrate, the content will still need to be counted into the dietary prescription.

Stock: Powder and cubes are used to flavour, soups, casseroles and sauces. Gluten free versions have less carbohydrate than the regular types.

Ice cream: Versions without added sugar are available and can be incorporated into the diet, however they need to be counted as part of the meal design. Oil, cream and butter can be mixed into ice cream to disguise their taste and increase the fat content.

Sweeteners:
Powder and tablet: Best for sweetening drinks. Small amounts (such as the amount used to sweeten a single drink) can be incorporated freely into the diet, however, large quantities need to be counted. They are not suitable for baking.
Liquid: Ideal for use in baking. It is best to use a small amount to avoid a bitter aftertaste. You may need to experiment a little to get the right amount.

Chocolate: Small amounts of dairy free/sugar free chocolate can be incorporated into the diet. It is usually grated in baking (sugar free dark chocolate) or sprinkled over a dessert or snack (sugar free chocolate). These chocolates have a carbohydrate content of 9-10%.

Formula feeding and the ketogenic diet

Some infants and older individuals with significant disability require a predominantly liquid diet. This may be because they are young and have not yet started on solid food, or because they require nasogastric or gastrostomy feeding. The ketogenic diet can be given in a liquid form even more easily than as a solid diet. The liquid can be made up in the right proportions and given in even amounts throughout the day or sometimes continuously with the assistance of a feeding pump.

For the formula fed child requiring a ketogenic diet, specific nutrient amounts are calculated using the same principles employed for calculating the orally consumed, solid food diet. The formula of choice is based on the child's ketogenic diet prescription, the availability of products and the optimal route of administration. Sometimes a child may have a mixed diet comprising small solid meals and formula.

There are two approaches to using formula. The first is based on making up the feed from individual products according to the requirements and type of ketogenic diet of the child. This is based on individual fat, protein, and carbohydrate modules, plus vitamins and minerals, and electrolytes in required amounts. These modular feeds are better suited to the tube fed child than the orally fed child as their palatability can be an issue.

Below is an example of a Modular tube feed for the Classical ketogenic diet.

Modular tube feed for the Classical ketogenic diet	400g RCF® (Ross Metabolics) 88g Calogen® (SHS)* 4g Paediatric Seravit (SHS)* Electrolytes (if necessary) + water up to 1250ml

Above provides 731kcal and 16g protein

Totals:	73g fat
	16g protein
	2.6g carbohydrate
Diet Ratio:	73g fat: 18.6g protein + carbohydrate
	~ 4:1

The second approach is to use a ready made formula which is nutritionally complete. One example is Ketocal® (Scientific Hospital Supplies International) which is designed for the Classical ketogenic diet. It is a powdered formula with a 4:1 ratio of long chain fat to carbohydrate and protein. An infant formula in a 3:1 ratio is available in some countries.

Ketocal® is palatable and therefore suitable for oral as well as enteral tube feeding. Below is an example of a feed made from Ketocal®

Nutritionally complete formula feed for the Classical ketogenic diet	100g Ketocal®
	+ water to 1250ml
	Above feed provides 730kcal and 15.3g protein

Totals:	73g fat
	15.3g protein
	3.0g carbohydrate
Diet Ratio:	73g fat: 18.3g protein + carbohydrate
	= 4:1

Weaning the diet

Just like any anti-epileptic drug, the diet should not be stopped abruptly. The diet should be weaned in a planned manner with the help of your ketogenic diet team. With the Classical ketogenic diet, the ratio of fat to protein + carbohydrate (CHO) is lowered over a specified period of time. For the MCT diet, the contribution of fat to the total calorie prescription is gradually reduced. This means that foods containing significant amounts of protein and CHO are added to the diet, and foods comprising mainly of fat are reduced. The total calorie prescription should be kept fairly stable during the weaning process. In this way, the impact on growth is minimised.

There are four main reasons that the ketogenic diet is weaned:

1 A child has been on the diet for two years with good effect. Parents in this situation are keen to see if their child will have seizure control without the diet.

2 A child has not benefited significantly from the diet and so a decision to stop the diet is made.

3 A child is not coping with the diet and it has become very difficult to manage for the family.

4 A child is experiencing intolerable side effects that cannot be resolved.

Understandably, most parents have very mixed feelings about weaning their child's diet. For some it is a relief as they realise their child will eat a normal diet and participate in activities without the planning and thought that goes into every meal. For others it is an anxious time as it is difficult to predict whether seizures will return or whether the child will require a change in their medication. Because the ketogenic diet can have side effects, and imposes a rigid eating plan on a child's life, it is usually not considered a diet for life. Nearly all children on the diet will have a trial of weaning the diet. If weaning has been advised but you wish to continue the diet, discuss your concerns with the doctor.

How to wean

The program for weaning your child's diet will depend on several factors:

1 The effect that the diet has had on your child's seizures and the length of time your child has been on the diet. The greater the reduction in seizures, the longer it will take to wean the diet. If your child's seizures have been reduced by > 95% and they have been on the diet for approximately two years, weaning may take up to one year. This is also the case when they have been seizure free off medication for one year on the diet. If the diet has not been effective then weaning should only take a short period of time.

2 The general health of your child. If your child is unwell or experiencing side effects as a result of the diet, it may be necessary to wean the diet in a short period of time.

Two main weaning methods are available. One involves the gradual decrease of the ketogenic diet ratio, the other involves exchanging food.

Decreasing the ratio for the Classical ketogenic diet

This method is usually chosen when a child enjoys their ketogenic meals, and their carer finds the adjustment of ketogenic recipes an easy task. It is also the method of choice when the child has been on the diet for a long period of time and experienced a significant reduction in seizures.
   To decrease the ratio your dietitian will calculate new dietary fat, carbohydrate, and protein values, for each meal and snack. Your child's recipes then need to be adjusted using these new values.
   The length of time your child is at each lower ratio will depend on your child's compliance, the wishes of your family, your child's seizure activity as the diet is weaned, anti-epileptic drug regimen, your child's health and growth, and any side effects resulting from the diet. This will be planned with your ketogenic diet team.

Food exchanging	This method is usually chosen when a child is keen to have non-ketogenic type foods introduced into their diet. Parents who do not wish to recalculate their recipes also prefer this method.

Generally ketogenic meals and snacks contain large amounts of oil, cream, butter and margarine. Your dietitian will give you advice on how to decrease the amounts of these high fat foods and how to increase other nutrient components such as protein and carbohydrate appropriately.

MCT weaning	MCT diet weaning uses the same basic principles that weaning the Classical ketogenic diet employs; the amount of fat (in this case largely MCT) is slowly reduced, while protein and carbohydrate are increased.

A stepwise process can be used such as in the example below:

1 Decrease MCT fat by 5-15g per day; weekly (or longer) or per meal/snack (depending on amount in initial prescription).

2 Increase protein exchanges by 1 per day; weekly (or longer) until normal size protein portions are achieved, then allow freely.

3 Increase carbohydrate exchanges by 1 per day; weekly (or longer) until normal size portions are achieved, then also allow freely.

It is important to aim for a normal fat intake as a proportion of the daily total energy requirement. To achieve this, additional LCT fat may be required to ensure adequate calorie provision during the transition to a normal diet and whilst the MCT fat is being reduced. This is more likely to be necessary for an MCT diet being weaned where MCT fat makes up a very high percentage of the total fat content.

Monitoring	Regardless of the method for weaning used, your child's ketone levels must be monitored regularly. This is particularly important when a change is made. A normal diet can be started when ketones are no longer being produced. This is likely to occur when your child's diet is providing about 80% of the total energy as fat (2:1 ratio) or when MCT fat is no longer being consumed.

Recipes

Classical ketogenic diet recipes
Breakfast

Porridge

This recipe takes a little practice however it is worth persevering as the result is a lovely creamy porridge your child will enjoy. Feel free to vary the water amount to suit your child's preference. We used "traditional" rather than "quick cook" oats as they go further!

Ingredient:	3:1	3.5:1	4:1
rolled oats	7g	6g	4g
water	70ml	60ml	50ml
rice bran oil	23g	27g	27g
whole egg, beaten	44g	44g	44g
liquid artificial sweetener	optional	optional	optional
thickened cream (35% fat)	26g	26g	27g
	makes 1 serve providing 383kcal, 6.9g protein	makes 1 serve providing 416kcal, 6.8g protein	makes 1 serve providing 411kcal, 6.7g protein

Method

1 Place oats into a small microwave safe bowl with the water.

2 Place the bowl into the microwave and cook on a low setting (160W) for 2½ minutes. The oats should have softened.

3 Add the oil, beaten egg, and artificial sweetener, if using.

4 Return the porridge back to the microwave and cook for a further 3½ minutes on a low setting (160W). Stir the porridge at 1 minute intervals during the cooking.

5 Serve the porridge with thickened cream on top.

Variation: Butter may replace some of the cream and oil if your child prefers.

French toast

Ingredient:	3:1	3.5:1	4:1
clotted cream (60% fat)	24g	24g	24g
whole egg, beaten	16g	16g	16g
vintage cheddar cheese (37% fat)	11g	9g	–
rice bran oil	19g	19g	19g
white bread, crusts removed	14g	11g	11g
	makes 1 serve providing 411kcal, 6.0g protein	makes 1 serve providing 395kcal, 5.3g protein	makes 1 serve providing 357kcal, 3.2g protein

Method

1 In a small bowl mix together clotted cream, egg and cheese (for 3:1 and 3.5:1 recipes).

2 Heat rice bran oil in a small non-stick frying pan over a medium heat.

3 Dip bread into the cream and egg mixture until the bread is completely saturated and all of the mixture is adhering to the bread (it may be necessary to add some to the bread during cooking). Cook in the frying pan and sizzle until crisp on one side. Carefully flip toast over and cook on the other side.

NB: When both sides are cooked the oil should be completely absorbed.

Mains
Eggs

Bacon and egg

Ingredient:	3:1	3.5:1	4:1
rice bran oil	17g	20g	24g
bacon, middle rasher	18g	18g	18g
whole egg	20g	20g	20g
sour cream (38% fat)	27g	28g	28g
vintage cheddar cheese (37% fat)	20g	14g	11g
	makes 1 serve providing 388kcal, 11.6g protein	makes 1 serve providing 393kcal, 10.3g protein	makes 1 serve providing 416kcal, 9.6g protein

Method

1 Place rice bran oil into a small non-stick frying pan and heat to medium.

2 Cook bacon rasher until brown and crisp as desired. Remove from the pan.

3 Stir together the beaten egg and sour cream. Pour mixture into the heated frying pan and cook until the egg has almost set.

4 Add cheese and cook until completely set.

5 Serve egg with bacon on the side.

Omelette and fruit dessert

Ingredient:	3:1	3.5:1	4:1
banana, sliced	10g	8g	8g
watermelon, cubed	40g	35g	35g
clotted cream	26g	28g	28g
tomato, chopped	15g	15g	15g
mushroom, thinly sliced	15g	15g	31g
whole egg, beaten	44g	36g	30g
clotted cream, extra	5g	5g	5g
butter	8g	8g	8g
olive oil	8g	8g	11g
	makes 1 serve providing 394kcal, 7.4g protein	makes 1 serve providing 391kcal, 6.4g protein	makes 1 serve providing 410kcal, 5.6g protein

Method

1 Place banana and watermelon into a small bowl with the clotted cream and chill.

2 Mix together tomato, mushroom, egg and extra cream in a medium sized bowl.

3 Melt butter and oil together in a small non-stick frying pan and add omelette mixture. Cook until set.

4 Serve with chilled banana, watermelon and cream.

Beef and pork

Beef stroganoff

Ingredient:	3:1	3.5:1	4:1
tomato	120g	100g	100g
mushroom	115g	115g	114g
zucchini	80g	80g	80g
red capsicum	80g	80g	80g
onion	20g	20g	20g
rice bran oil	70g	82g	90g
beef mince (15% fat)	87g	74g	56g
tomato paste	35g	35g	35g
sour cream (35% fat)	100g	100g	100g
	makes 4 serves each providing 314kcal, 6.8g protein	makes 4 serves each providing 334kcal, 6.2g protein	makes 4 serves each providing 343kcal, 5.3g protein

Method

1 Using a sharp knife thinly slice tomato, mushroom, zucchini, capsicum and onion.

2 Gently heat oil in a medium sized, non-stick frying pan. Add sliced vegetables and cook slowly until the vegetables are nearly tender and the oil is almost absorbed.

3 Add mince to the pan and cook, covered, until meat and vegetables are tender. Stir in tomato paste and simmer for 5-10 minutes.

4 Stir through cream and serve immediately.

Bacon quiche

Ingredient:	3:1	3.5:1	4:1
red capsicum	100g	100g	100g
brown onion	120g	120g	120g
tomato	120g	120g	120g
zucchini	320g	320g	320g
carrot, peeled	80g	80g	80g
bacon, short rindless	120g	120g	120g
double thick cream	192g	192g	208g
whole egg, beaten	120g	120g	88g
rice bran oil	124g	124g	140g
banana, peeled	60g	–	–
	makes 8 serves each providing 337kcal, 6.2g protein	makes 8 serves each providing 331kcal, 6.1g protein	makes 8 serves each providing 353kcal, 5.6g protein

Method

1 Preheat oven to hot (200°C).

2 Finely slice capsicum, onion and tomato. Grate zucchini and carrot. Finely chop bacon.

3 Mix all of the above prepared ingredients together with cream, egg and oil.

4 Pour mixture into a 23cm round flan dish.

5 Cook in heated oven for 30 minutes and until lightly browned on top.

Bacon and zucchini fettuccine

Ingredient:	3:1	3.5:1	4:1
rice bran oil	88g	104g	124g
bacon, middle rasher	76g	68g	60g
zucchini, grated or sliced	100g	100g	100g
fettuccine, low carbohydrate, boiled weight	150g	140g	140g
pesto, classic basil	40g	40g	40g
clotted cream	92g	92g	92g
	makes 4 serves each providing 438kcal, 6.5g protein	makes 4 serves each providing 467kcal, 6g protein	makes 8 serves each providing 511kcal, 5.4g protein

Method

1 Place oil in a large non-stick frying pan. Heat to medium.

2 Fry bacon until almost crisp. Add zucchini and fry until softened.

3 Place fettuccine in a medium sized bowl and stir through pesto and half the clotted cream.

4 Add remaining cream to zucchini and bacon and serve on top of fettuccine.

Ham and cheese salad

Ingredient:	3:1	3.5:1	4:1
iceberg lettuce	60g	60g	60g
tomato	50g	50g	50g
carrot, peeled	30g	30g	30g
deli leg ham, lean	15g	12g	10g
vintage cheddar cheese (37% fat)	18g	15g	13g
olive oil	5g	6g	6g
mayonnaise (>80% fat)	28g	30g	34g
herbed seasoning salt	to taste	to taste	to taste
	makes 1 serve providing 365kcal, 8.6g protein	makes 1 serve providing 372kcal, 7.4g protein	makes 1 serve providing 392kcal, 6.6g protein

Method

1 Using a sharp knife thinly slice lettuce and tomato. Grate carrot.

2 Finely dice ham and allow cheese to crumble.

3 Combine above in a serving bowl.

4 Toss salad with oil. Serve with mayonnaise and herbed seasoning salt if desired.

Chicken and fish

Chicken stir fry

Stir fries are often eaten by children on the ketogenic diet for lunch and dinner. Lots of children even eat them for breakfast! Experiment with this recipe and come up with something that your child really loves.

Ingredient:	3:1	3.5:1	4:1
red capsicum	25g	25g	25g
carrot, peeled	41g	41g	41g
onion, peeled	10g	10g	10g
green beans	35g	33g	33g
rice bran oil	35g	39g	42g
chicken breast, lean	26g	24g	21g
	makes 1 serve providing 370kcal, 7.6g protein	makes 1 serve providing 403kcal, 7.1g protein	makes 1 serve providing 426kcal, 6.4g protein

Method

1 Using a sharp knife or V-slice, thinly slice capsicum, carrot, onion and green beans.

2 Gently heat oil in a non-stick frying pan. Add sliced vegetables and cook slowly until the vegetables are nearly tender and the oil is almost absorbed.

3 Chop chicken and add to the pan. Cook until tender.

Variation: Substitute one of the vegetables for very finely sliced cabbage (red, white or Chinese). Because cabbage is low in carbohydrate the meal is bulkier; and it is very high in fibre. For a truly Asian flavour incorporate sesame oil into the recipe. Use beef or pork instead of the chicken as a meat alternative.

Chicken and vegetable patties with fruit dessert

Ingredient:	3:1	3.5:1	4:1
strawberries	200g	200g	200g
zucchini, grated	160g	160g	160g
chicken breast raw, lean	77g	54g	44g
macadamia nuts, ground to meal	47g	47g	47g
clotted cream (60% fat)	24g	24g	32g
whole egg, beaten	36g	36g	36g
butter	15g	20g	28g
rice bran oil	40g	40g	40g
clotted cream, extra	32g	32g	32g
	makes 4 serves each providing 332kcal, 7.8g protein	makes 4 serves each providing 335kcal, 6.5g protein	makes 4 serves each providing 358kcal, 6.0g protein

Method

1 Wash and trim strawberries. Chill.

2 Add zucchini to very finely diced chicken in a large bowl. Add macadamia meal, cream and beaten egg. Mix well.

3 Gently heat butter and oil in a medium sized, non-stick frying pan.
Spoon dessertspoons of the mixture into the frying pan (should make 8 patties).

4 The patties are cooked when both sides are lightly browned. Serve with chilled strawberries and extra cream.

Chicken kebab with coleslaw and avocado dip

Ingredient:	3:1	3.5:1	4:1
cabbage, white	56g	56g	55g
carrot, peeled	50g	50g	50g
chives, dried	½ tsp	½ tsp	½ tsp
mayonnaise (>80% fat)	50g	50g	50g
lemon juice	6g	6g	6g
avocado	65g	60g	60g
sour cream	25g	32g	40g
celery	50g	40g	40g
chicken breast, lean	51g	39g	30g
	makes 2 serves each providing 343kcal, 7.8g protein	makes 2 serves each providing 343kcal, 6.4g protein	makes 2 serves each providing 352kcal, 5.5g protein

Method

Coleslaw

Using a sharp knife or 'V-slice', finely slice cabbage and carrot. Mix together with chives.

Mayonnaise

1 Add the lemon juice to the mayonnaise. Place into a serving bowl.

2 Use ¾ of mayonnaise to dress the coleslaw. Put remaining mayonnaise and dressed coleslaw into the refrigerator.

Avocado dip

1 Blend avocado and sour cream with remaining mayonnaise.

2 Slice celery into thin lengths for dipping.

Kebab

1 Using a sharp knife, dice chicken breast and pan fry until cooked (a very quick spray of oil is allowed and does not need to be included in calculations).

2 Place cooked chicken onto a small bamboo stick (or toothpick) which has been soaked in water for 10 minutes.

Serve dressed coleslaw, kebab and celery on a plate. Place bowl containing dip on side. Eat kebab and celery with avocado dip.

Satay chicken

Ingredient:	3:1	3.5:1	4:1
eggplant	100g	100g	100g
zucchini	120g	120g	120g
red capsicum	120g	120g	120g
carrot, peeled	100g	100g	97g
rice bran oil	60g	60g	60g
garlic salt (optional)	to taste	to taste	to taste
chicken breast, lean	84g	64g	44g
peanut butter (53% fat)	20g	20g	20g
butter	45g	50g	50g
coconut essence	1 tsp	1 tsp	1 tsp
double thick cream	30g	37g	54g
rockmelon	100g	100g	100g
clotted cream	60g	70g	70g
	makes 4 serves each providing 423kcal, 7.5g protein	makes 4 serves each providing 450kcal, 6.5g protein	makes 4 serves each providing 466kcal, 5.4g protein

Method

1 Using a sharp knife thinly slice, then chop into small pieces, the eggplant and zucchini. Cut the capsicum into very thin strips. Grate the carrot.

2 Gently heat oil in a large non-stick frying pan. Add vegetables and garlic salt

(if using) and cook slowly until the vegetables are nearly tender and the oil is almost absorbed.

3   Add chicken to the pan and cook, covered until tender.   Stir in butters and coconut essence and gently simmer for 10 minutes.

4 Stir through double thick cream. Serve with chopped rockmelon topped with clotted cream.

Variation This dish could be made into a satay salad. Cook only the eggplant in oil and allow to cool. Leave the other vegetables raw and top with cooked chicken and warmed sauces.

Salmon and vegetable medley

Ingredient:	3:1	3.5:1	4:1
broccoli	40g	40g	40g
zucchini	112g	112g	112g
rice bran oil	20g	26g	32g
red salmon, canned in brine, drained	88g	72g	72g
cream cheese	77g	77g	77g
sour cream (38% fat)	36g	36g	50g
clotted cream	60g	63g	78g
	makes 4 serves each providing 276kcal, 7.7g protein	makes 4 serves each providing 286kcal, 6.8g protein	makes 4 serves each providing 333kcal, 6.9g protein

Method

1 Using a sharp knife or a V-slice, slice broccoli and grate zucchini.

2 Gently heat oil in a medium sized, non-stick frying pan.

3 Add vegetables to the pan and cook slowly until the vegetables are nearly tender.

4 Add salmon to the pan and heat to desired temperature.

5 Stir in cheese and creams.

6 Bake under grill until browned and bubbling on top.

Vegetarian

Vegetable laksa

Ingredient:	3:1	3.5:1	4:1
rice bran oil	60g	68g	85g
onion, finely chopped	50g	40g	40g
ground ginger	1 teaspoon	1 teaspoon	1 teaspoon
chilli powder	1 teaspoon	1 teaspoon	1 teaspoon
ground cumin	1 teaspoon	1 teaspoon	1 teaspoon
ground coriander	1 teaspoon	1 teaspoon	1 teaspoon
garam masala	½ teaspoon	½ teaspoon	½ teaspoon
pumpkin, peeled and chopped	370g	370g	370g
gluten free vegetable stock cube	3g	3g	3g
boiling water	300ml	300ml	300ml
coconut cream (28% fat)	200g	200g	200g
green beans, halved	160g	100g	100g
	makes 4 serves each providing 303kcal, 3.8g protein	makes 4 serves each providing 317kcal, 3.4g protein	makes 4 serves each providing 355kcal, 3.4g protein

Method 1 Heat oil in a large non-stick frying pan over a low heat. Cook onion, stirring until it softens. Add spices; cook, stirring about 2 minutes or until fragrant. Add pumpkin; stir to coat in the spice mixture.

2 Dissolve stock cube in water. Stir stock and coconut cream in with the vegetables; bring to the boil. Reduce heat; simmer, covered, about 20 minutes or until pumpkin is almost tender. If necessary, add a little extra water. Stir in green beans, simmer, covered, about 5 minutes or until pumpkin is tender. Remove from heat and serve.

Variations: Experiment with different vegetables; cauliflower, spinach, tomato and red capsicum all add colour and taste good. Vary the spices. The ground spices are not included in the diet ratio and so you can omit some/all if your child prefers.

Zucchini and fetta pancakes

Ingredient:	3:1	3.5:1	4:1
egg white	80g	72g	65g
egg yolk	60g	47g	43g
zucchini, grated	200g	200g	185g
feta cheese (27% fat)	80g	80g	65g
clotted cream	18g	18g	25g
macadamia nuts, ground to meal	60g	60g	60g
fresh mint	1 tablespoon	1 tablespoon	1 tablespoon
salt and pepper	to taste	to taste	to taste
butter	12g	20g	20g
rice bran oil	36g	44g	50g
sour cream	20g	30g	30g
	makes 4 serves each providing 383kcal, 9.9g protein	makes 4 serves each providing 414kcal, 9.3g protein	makes 4 serves each providing 421kcal, 8.2g protein

Method

1 Beat the egg white until stiff.

2 In a medium-sized bowl, combine egg yolk, zucchini, feta cheese, clotted cream, macadamia meal, mint, and seasonings. Mix well.

3 Fold the egg whites into the zucchini mixture.

4 Heat the butter and the oil over a low heat (if making 4 separate serves divide portions of butter and oil accordingly), in a very large non-stick frying pan. When it is heated add spoonfuls of the batter, and fry on both sides until golden and crisp.

5 Serve immediately, topped with sour cream.

Ratatouille

Ingredient:	3:1	3.5:1	4:1
olive oil	20g	20g	20g
rice bran oil	54g	54g	54g
eggplant, chopped	100g	100g	100g
salt and black pepper	to taste	to taste	to taste
mushrooms, sliced	40g	40g	40g
red capsicum, sliced	50g	50g	50g
green capsicum, sliced	50g	50g	50g
bottled tomato pasta sauce	100g	100g	100g
dried mixed herbs	1 teaspoon	1 teaspoon	1 teaspoon
fettuccine, low carbohydrate boiled weight	40g	18g	–
sour cream (37% fat)	40g	40g	40g
	makes 2 serves each providing 470kcal, 4.0g protein	makes 2 serves each providing 460kcal, 3.5g protein	makes 2 serves each providing 451kcal, 3.2 protein

Method

1 Heat oils in a medium sized non-stick frying pan. Add eggplant and salt and pepper. Cook over medium heat, stirring often until eggplant is almost soft. Add mushrooms and cook until they are almost soft. Most of the oil will be absorbed at this step.

2 Add red and green capsicum, bottled tomato sauce and mixed herbs. Continue to simmer over a low heat, covered until all the vegetables are tender; approximately 20 minutes (if using fettuccine add after this point).

3 Serve hot with sour cream.

Eggplant fettuccine

Ingredient:	3:1	3.5:1	4:1
rice bran oil	110g	122g	132g
eggplant, sliced	120g	120g	120g
tomato, chopped	40g	40g	40g
fettuccine, low carbohydrate, boiled weight	153g	153g	140g
pesto, classic basil	40g	40g	40g
parmesan cheese, grated	10g	–	–
	makes 4 serves each providing 346kcal, 3.4g protein	makes 4 serves each providing 362kcal, 2.4g protein	makes 4 serves each providing 382kcal, 2.3g protein

Method

1 Place oil in a large non-stick frying pan. Heat to medium.

2 Fry eggplant until softened and almost crisp. Add tomato and cook for a further 5 minutes.

3 Place fettuccine in a medium sized bowl and stir through pesto.

4 Top fettuccine with eggplant and tomato (and parmesan if in allowance).

"I want takeaway tonight"

Chicken wrap with ice-cream whip

Ingredient:	3:1	3.5:1	4:1
rice bran oil	27g	31g	34g
no added sugar vanilla ice cream, softened	80g	69g	64g
rice bran oil, extra	15g	15g	20g
chicken, tempura medallion, room temperature	55g	50g	50g
mayonnaise (>80% fat)	29g	29g	29g
lettuce	2 leaves	2 leaves	2 leaves
	makes 2 serves each providing 389kcal, 6.0g protein	makes 2 serves each providing 398kcal, 5.4g protein	makes 2 serves each providing 432kcal, 5.2g protein

Method

1 Mix the rice bran oil into ice-cream until evenly distributed. Place in freezer to set.

2 Heat extra oil in a small non-stick frying pan over a medium heat.

3 Cook chicken until covering has just crisped, and chicken is tender.

4 Place ¼ of the chicken onto ½ a lettuce leaf; dollop with ¼ of the mayonnaise.

5 Wrap leaf around chicken and mayonnaise.

6 Repeat steps 4 and 5 with remaining chicken, lettuce and mayonnaise.

7 Serve 2 wraps with ½ of the ice-cream whip (for 1 serve).

Pizza

Basic pizza base

Ingredient:	3:1	3.5:1	4:1
macadamia nuts, ground into meal	54g	50g	46g
almond meal	30g	20g	14g
thickened cream	30g	30g	30g
whole egg, beaten	48g	40g	34g
olive oil	10g	12g	14g
	makes 1 serve providing 842kcal, 17.4g protein	makes 1 serve providing 758kcal, 14g protein	makes 1 serve providing 700kcal, 11.6g protein

Method

1 Preheat oven to 180°C.

2 Line a square or rectangular oven tray with baking paper.

3 Mix all of the ingredients until they come together in a "dough" like consistency.

4 Press the dough into a circle onto the baking paper so that it is ½cm thick.

5 Cook base for 10-15 minutes; until firm and slightly golden.

6 Leave oven on while preparing the topping.

Pizza topping suggestions

Supreme

Ingredient:	3:1	3.5:1	4:1
onion, thinly sliced or grated	28g	28g	28g
mushroom, thinly sliced	28g	28g	28g
tomato	40g	40g	40g
lean beef sausage	20g	20g	20g
bacon, middle rasher lean	36g	30g	24g
vintage cheddar cheese (37% fat)	40g	40g	40g
olive oil	52g	60g	66g
	makes 1 serve providing 756kcal, 21.2g protein	makes 1 serve providing 820kcal, 19.8g protein	makes 1 serve providing 866kcal, 18.6g protein
combined with base above	makes 2 pizzas each providing 799kcal, 19.3g protein	makes 2 pizzas each providing 789kcal, 16.9g protein	makes 2 pizzas each providing 788kcal, 15.1g protein

Method

1 Spread all ingredients except for the olive oil evenly over the pizza base.

2 Bake in the oven until the cheese melts and the sausage and bacon start to crisp; approximately 10 minutes.

3 Remove the cooked pizza from the oven and immediately, evenly spread the olive oil over the pizza (while it is hot the oil will be easily absorbed).

Tuna

Ingredient:	3:1	3.5:1	4:1
onion, thinly sliced or grated	10g	10g	10g
capsicum, green, thinly sliced or grated	10g	10g	16g
tomato, chopped	20g	20g	40g
tuna, canned in oil and drained	23g	19g	30g
vintage cheddar cheese (37% fat)	20g	20g	20g
olive oil	25g	28g	60g
	makes 1 serve providing 734kcal, 21.5g protein	makes 1 serve providing 771kcal, 19.5g protein	makes 1 serve providing 789kcal, 17.6g protein
combined with base above	makes 2 pizzas each providing 788kcal, 19.5g protein	makes 2 pizzas each providing 765kcal, 16.8g protein	makes 2 pizzas each providing 745kcal, 14.6g protein

Method

1 Spread all ingredients except for the olive oil evenly over the pizza base. Bake in the oven until the cheese melts, approximately 10 minutes.

2 Remove the cooked pizza from the oven and immediately, evenly spread the olive oil over the pizza (while it is hot the oil will be easily absorbed).

NB: In all of the above pizza recipes, some olive oil can be replaced with rice bran oil if preferred.

Suggestions: Combinations of the following ingredients: sliced olives, sautéed mushrooms, kabana, salami, feta cheese, sautéed capsicum, tomato, roasted pumpkin, spinach leaves and more......

Zucchini slice with tomato salsa

Ingredient:	3:1	3.5:1	4:1
zucchini, grated	150g	150g	150g
whole egg, beaten	100g	100g	100g
macadamia nuts, ground to meal	40g	40g	40g
clotted cream	53g	68g	80g
parmesan cheese (33% fat)	53g	38g	27g
dried basil, oregano and/or rosemary (optional)	pinches	pinches	pinches
rice bran oil	–	–	20g
olive oil	40g	40g	20g
tomato, chopped	160g	150g	140g
olive oil, extra	14g	15g	16g
	makes 4 serves each providing 378kcal, 9.9g protein	makes 4 serves each providing 381kcal, 8.5g protein	makes 4 serves each providing 387kcal, 7.5g protein

Method

1 Pre-heat oven to 200°C. Grease a 25cm spring-form baking pan and line the base with baking paper.

2 Combine zucchini, egg, macadamia meal, clotted cream, parmesan, herbs and half of the total oil in a bowl and mix well.

3 Spread into the prepared pan and bake until golden brown; approximately 20 minutes. About halfway through the baking, brush with the remaining oil.

4 Remove from the oven. When the base has cooled for 10 minutes, remove from pan. Combine chopped tomato with extra olive oil.

5 Serve slice with tomato salsa.

Hamburger and fruit dessert

Ingredient:	3:1	3.5:1	4:1
"Bun"			
whole egg, beaten	22g	22g	22g
clotted cream	16g	16g	28g
rice bran oil	7g	9g	11g
"Burger"			
beef, mince (15% fat)	37g	37g	37g
zucchini, grated	20g	20g	20g
carrot, grated	8g	8g	8g
whole egg, beaten	9g	9g	9g
rice bran oil	2g	2g	3g
tomato cooking sauce	5g	5g	5g
avocado	25g	25g	25g
tomato	7g	7g	7g
mayonnaise (>80% fat)	5g	5g	7g
low carbohydrate tomato sauce	5g	5g	5g
lettuce	1 leaf	1 leaf	1 leaf

"Dessert"			
clotted cream	25g	25g	25g
rice bran oil	5g	8g	10g
low carbohydrate jelly and fruit	120g	120g	120g
low carbohydrate chocolate topping	6g	6g	6g
	makes 1 serve providing 611kcal, 14g protein	makes 1 serve providing 639kcal, 12.5g protein	makes 1serve providing 727kcal, 12.6g protein

Method
Bun

1 Combine raw egg, clotted cream and rice bran oil in a small bowl.

2 Pour ½ mixture into a pre-heated non-stick frying pan. Cook over medium heat, until lightly browned both sides.

3 Repeat with remaining batter.

This will make 2 small crepes resembling the "bun".

Burger

1 Combine minced beef, zucchini, carrot, egg, rice bran oil and tomato cooking sauce in a small bowl. Use hands to form a patty.

2 Cook patty in heated, non-stick frying pan, until browned on both sides and cooked through.

3 Sandwich patty, avocado, tomato, mayonnaise, low-carbohydrate tomato sauce and lettuce between crepes.

Dessert

1 Serve combined cream and oil over jelly and fruit. Top with chocolate topping.

Desserts

Strawberry mousse

Ingredient:	3:1	3.5:1	4:1
gelatine	5g	5g	5g
water	125ml	125ml	125ml
strawberries, stems removed	240g	240g	240g
double thick cream	250g	250g	250g
lemon juice	48g	48g	20g
liquid artificial sweetener	equivalent to ½ cup sugar	equivalent to ½ cup sugar	equivalent to ½ cup sugar
vanilla essence	2 tsp	2 tsp	2 tsp
egg white	84g	84g	84g
banana, peeled	25g	22g	–
	makes 6 serves each providing 237kcal, 3.8g protein	makes 6 serves each providing 233kcal, 3.8g protein	makes 6 serves each providing 230kcal, 3.7g protein

Method

1 Sprinkle gelatine over surface of water in a small saucepan and allow to rest for 5 minutes.

2 Place strawberries, cream, lemon juice, liquid sugar substitute and vanilla essence into a blender.

3 Heat gelatine and water while stirring until gelatine is completely dissolved. Add to other ingredients in blender and blend until all of the ingredients are well combined.

4 Beat egg whites until soft peaks form. Fold the egg whites into the strawberry mixture until combined.

5 Divide mixture into 6 serving dishes.

6 Refrigerate until set. Serve chilled (with banana when indicated).

Chocolate mousse

Ingredient:	3:1	3.5:1	4:1
thickened cream 35% fat	74g	57g	57g
water	180ml	180ml	180ml
gelatine	5g	5g	5g
cocoa powder (sweetened)	26g	26g	26g
water, extra	60ml	60ml	60ml
egg yolk	104g	32g	32g
egg white	–	73g	73g
double thick cream	250g	250g	250g
liquid artificial sweetener	to taste	to taste	to taste
milk chocolate, grated	23g	10g	–
	makes 6 serves each providing 304kcal, 5g protein	makes 6 serves each providing 292kcal, 4.8g protein	makes 6 serves each providing 284kcal, 4.7g protein

Method

1 Mix the thickened cream with 125ml of the water to make a "milk" type liquid. Heat "milk" until almost boiling then set aside to cool slightly.

2 Sprinkle gelatine over the remaining 60ml water and leave to rest until required.

3 Heat cocoa and extra water in a medium-sized saucepan, stirring, until a smooth paste is achieved. Whisk yolks into this paste.

Chocolate mousse

4 Add "milk" to this mixture and stir slowly. Heat and stir constantly over a medium heat until this mixture thickens slightly. Do not allow mixture to boil. Remove from heat.

5 Heat gelatine and water, stirring, until gelatine is completely dissolved. Mix dissolved gelatine, double thick cream, and sugar substitute into the thickened chocolate milk mixture. Cover surface with plastic film and refrigerate for at least 30 minutes.

6 Beat the egg whites until soft peaks form. Gently fold egg whites into the refrigerated chocolate milk mixture.

7 Divide mixture into 6 serving dishes. Refrigerate until set and serve (with equal amount grated chocolate if indicated).

Strawberries, cream, chocolate and nuts
photographed next page

Ingredient:	3:1	3.5:1	4:1
strawberries, chopped	34g	32g	30g
clotted cream	16g	19g	21g
dairy free chocolate, melted	19g	14g	12g
pistachio nuts, chopped thinly	8g	6g	4g
	makes 1 serve providing 226kcal, 3.6g protein	makes 1 serve providing 209kcal, 2.9g protein	makes 1 serve providing 200kcal, 2.4g protein

Method

1 Place strawberries into serving dish. Spoon cream over the strawberries.

2 Pour melted chocolate over the cream and strawberries (use a small spatula to ensure that all of the chocolate is used). Sprinkle with nuts and serve.

Strawberries, cream, chocolate and nuts

Chocolate slice

Chocolate slice
photographed previous page

This slice is delicious served warm with cream or ice-cream allowance on top. Enjoy!

Ingredient:	3:1	3.5:1	4:1
butter	125g	125g	125g
rice bran oil	40g	40g	40g
cocoa powder, sweetened	35g	35g	35g
egg yolk	72g	72g	72g
egg white	67g	67g	67g
desiccated coconut	50g	50g	50g
almond meal	50g	50g	50g
liquid artificial sweetener	equivalent to 1 cup sugar	equivalent to 1 cup sugar	equivalent to 1 cup sugar
vanilla essence	to taste	to taste	to taste
thickened cream (35% fat)	–	–	80g
strawberries, chopped	–	200g	–
no added sugar vanilla ice-cream	125g	–	–
	makes 8 serves each providing 297kcal, 5.9g protein	makes 8 serves each providing 323kcal, 5.8g protein	makes 4 serves each providing 317kcal, 5.3g protein

Method

1 Preheat oven to 180°C. Line a 19cm x 19cm baking pan with baking paper.

2 Place the butter and oil in a small saucepan. Heat over a low heat until all butter has melted.

3 Sift cocoa powder into the butter and oil.

4 Place egg yolk into a medium sized bowl and beat with an electric beater until they are light in colour and a thick, creamy consistency; approximately 10 minutes.

5 Add the beaten yolks to the butter, oil and cocoa powder.

6 Add desiccated coconut, almond meal, liquid sugar substitute and vanilla essence to the butter, oil, cocoa powder and egg yolk. Mix until well combined.

7 Beat the egg whites in a small bowl until soft peaks form. Fold the egg whites into the slice mixture.

8 Bake in the oven for approximately 25 minutes. Allow to sit until cooled before removing from tray. This will ensure that any unabsorbed oil will melt into the slice and keep it moist.

9 Serve with thickened cream, strawberry or ice-cream allowance as indicated.

Apple crumble

Ingredient:	3:1	3.5:1	4:1
granny smith apple, peeled, grated	60g	54g	50g
rice bran oil	10g	12g	16g
blanched almonds, crushed	18g	12g	10g
desiccated coconut	18g	12g	10g
cinnamon	to taste	to taste	to taste
liquid artificial sweetener	to taste	to taste	to taste
double thick cream (55% fat)	20g	24g	24g
	makes 2 serves each providing 221kcal, 2.7g protein	makes 2 serves each providing 202kcal, 1.9g protein	makes 2 serves each providing 206kcal, 1.6g protein

Method

1 Preheat oven to moderate (180°C).

2 Mix grated apple and oil; place in a small ovenproof dish. Top with nuts, coconut, cinnamon and sweetener.

3 Bake for 15-20 minutes; until golden brown.

4 Divide into 2 equal sized serves and top with cream allowance.

Baked cheesecake

Ingredient:	3:1	3.5:1	4:1
cream cheese (room temperature)	120g	92g	64g
double thick cream (55% fat)	28g	58g	82g
sour cream	30g	26g	26g
whole egg, beaten	44g	44g	44g
butter	10g	10g	10g
liquid artificial sweetener	to taste	to taste	to taste
lemon essence	to taste	to taste	to taste
strawberries, chopped	120g	120g	120g
	makes 4 serves each providing 204kcal, 4.9g protein	makes 4 serves each providing 215kcal, 4.4g protein	makes 4 serves each providing 222kcal, 3.8g protein

Method

1 Preheat oven to 150°C. You will need a cake tin, large enough to hold 2 oven proof ramekins.

2 Mix together the cream cheese, double thick cream, sour cream and egg. Blend in the butter. Add artificial sweetener and lemon essence and mix well to combine.

4 Pour mixture evenly between 2 oven proof ramekins. Place ramekins into the large cake tin. Pour water into the cake tin until it is halfway up the sides of the ramekins. Bake until set; approximately 40 minutes.

5 Remove from the oven and allow to cool before topping with strawberries. Serve.

Variation Change fruit type or essence type depending on your child's preference.

Pancakes
Basic mixture

Ingredient:	3:1 amount	3.5:1	4:1 amount
almond meal	30g	20g	17g
macadamia nuts, ground to meal	10g	10g	14g
whole egg, beaten	33g	25g	25g
double thick cream (55% fat)	10g	15g	15g
water	20ml	20ml	20ml
butter	8g	8g	10g
clotted cream	10g	10g	10g
sugar free maple syrup	6g	4g	2g
	makes 2 pancakes each providing 413kcal, 9.6g protein	makes 2 pancakes each providing 424kcal, 8.7g protein	makes 2 pancakes each providing 225kcal, 4.2g protein

Method

1 Mix almond meal, ground macadamias, beaten egg, cream and water together.

2 Melt the butter in a large non-stick frying pan over a medium heat.

3 Pour ½ the batter into the frying pan; cook, until browned on both sides. Repeat with remaining batter.

4 Serve pancakes with clotted cream and maple syrup.

Variations Below are some ideas for great pancake toppings. The ingredients will need to be entered into your computer program to ensure that the energy and protein prescription, and diet ratio are correct.

1 Spread sugar free conserve (~10g) over the pancake. Extra cream will increase the ratio if required.

2 Add 4 strawberries, raspberries or blackberries to the basic mixture. These do not need to be counted and so are considered "free".

3 Add some grated raw apple to the basic mixture. Extra cream will increase the ratio if required.

Baking

Carrot muffins

Ingredient:	3:1	3.5:1	4:1
carrot, peeled, grated	18g	18g	18g
whole egg, beaten	25g	25g	25g
double thick cream (55% fat)	32g	32g	32g
almond meal	22g	22g	22g
vanilla essence	to taste	to taste	to taste
liquid artificial sweetener	to taste	to taste	to taste
carbohydrate free margarine	18g	19g	18g
cream cheese (33% fat)	20g	20g	–
pure icing sugar	4g	2g	–
pure lemon juice	1 teaspoon	1 teaspoon	–
	makes 2 muffins each providing 278kcal, 5.2g protein	makes 2 muffins each providing 278kcal, 5.2g protein	makes 2 muffins each providing 237kcal, 4.3g protein

Method

1 Preheat oven to moderate (180°C). Place 2 non-stick paper patty cases into a 12-hole (⅓ cup/80ml) muffin pan.

2 Place a tall beaker onto the gram scales (make sure the beaker is suitable to hold a hand held beater).

3 Measure egg, cream, almond meal, vanilla essence and artificial sweetener into the beaker. (It may be easiest to zero the gram scales between each ingredient addition). Blend ingredients using a hand held beater.

4 Measure grated carrot into the beaker and stir. Pour mixture into the patty cases and cook for 20-25 minutes.

5 For 4:1 ratio serve with margarine. For 3:1 and 3.5:1 ratios: soften cream cheese and mix with pure icing sugar and pure lemon juice. Spread evenly over top of muffins. (A portion of the margarine allowance can be added to cream cheese frosting if desired).

Variation Almond meal can be replaced with hazelnut meal. Pecan nuts can also be used; a food processor can grind them quickly to make a fine meal. Apple or pear can substitute for the carrot. Coconut can also be incorporated into the recipe; it can replace some of the almond meal.....experiment!

Banana and coconut muffins

Ingredient:	3:1	3.5:1	4:1
banana, mashed	37g	33g	33g
whole egg, beaten	26g	20g	15g
double thick cream (55% fat)	30g	30g	30g
rice bran oil	23g	23g	23g
almond meal	27g	16g	10g
macadamia nuts, ground to meal	15g	15g	15g
desiccated coconut	25g	25g	25g
butter, softened	10g	10g	10g
self raising flour	7g	5g	3g
ground cinnamon	½ teaspoon	½ teaspoon	½ teaspoon
	makes 4 muffins each providing 192kcal, 2.6g protein	makes 4 muffins each providing 219kcal, 2.6g protein	makes 4 muffins each providing 206kcal, 2.1g protein

Method

1 Preheat oven to moderate. Place 4 non-stick paper patty cases into a 12-hole (⅓ cup/80ml) muffin pan.

2 Place a tall beaker onto the gram scales (make sure the beaker is suitable to hold a hand held beater). Place banana, egg, cream, oil, meals, coconut, butter, self-raising flour and cinnamon into the beaker.

3 Blend ingredients using a hand held beater. Divide mixture evenly among patty cases and cook for 25-35 mins.

Pineapple muffins

Ingredient:	3:1	3.5:1	4:1
desiccated coconut	180g	180g	180g
macadamia nuts, ground into meal	300g	300g	300g
self raising flour	10g	10g	10g
ground cinnamon	1½ teaspoons	1½ teaspoons	1½ teaspoons
butter, unsalted, melted	50g	50g	50g
coconut cream (28% fat)	–	–	120g
milk, full cream	190g	190g	65g
whole eggs, beaten	100g	100g	100g
liquid artificial sweetener (optional)	to taste	to taste	to taste
pineapple, fresh, diced	200g	200g	200g
water	as needed	as needed	as needed
vanilla yoghurt, low fat	102g	–	–
	makes 16 muffins each providing 262kcal, 3.8g protein	makes 16 muffins each providing 256kcal, 3.5g protein	makes 16 muffins each providing 271kcal, 3.3g protein

Method

1 Preheat oven to moderate (180¢xC). Place 16 paper patty cases into 2, 8 hole muffin pans (⅓ cup/80ml).

2 Mix together dessicated coconut, macadamia meal, self raising flour and cinnamon in a large bowl.

3 Make a well in the centre and add the melted butter, coconut cream, milk, egg and artificial sweetener. Mix until just combined, then fold through pineapple and water.

4 Spoon mixture evenly into the paper patty cases (mixture should easily fall off spoon) and bake for 20-30 minutes, or until golden brown.

5 Serve warm (in case of 3:1 ratio divide yoghurt allowance into 12 equal sized amounts to serve with each muffin).

NB: 3:1and 3.5:1 recipes, add a little coconut essence for additional flavour if desired.

Chocolate muffins

Ingredient:	3:1	3.5:1	4:1
self raising flour	8g	6g	4g
rice bran oil	18g	20g	22g
whole egg, beaten	32g	28g	28g
almonds, raw with skin, ground to meal	28g	28g	28g
butter, room temperature	10g	10g	10g
chocolate, no added sugar, grated	28g	14g	10g
clotted cream	20g	20g	20g
	makes 2 muffins each providing 356kcal, 6.2g protein	makes 2 muffins each providing 328kcal, 5.4g protein	makes 2 muffins each providing 324kcal, 5.2g protein

Method

1 Preheat oven to 180°C. Place 2 non-stick paper patty cases in an 8-hole pan (⅓ cup/80ml).

2 Mix together flour, oil, egg, almond meal and butter until well combined.

3 Add grated chocolate and divide mixture into the 2 cases. Bake for 20 minutes or until cooked through.

4 Serve each muffin warm with half of the clotted cream.

Cheese and spinach muffins

Ingredient:	3:1 amount	3.5:1	4:1 amount
whole egg, beaten	65g	47g	40g
fresh english spinach	43g	43g	43g
sour cream	30g	40g	50g
almond meal	60g	50g	44g
carbohydrate free margarine	36g	36g	36g
vintage cheddar cheese (37% fat), grated	50g	40g	30g
double thick cream (55% fat)	48g	56g	64g
	makes 4 muffins each providing 325kcal, 8.9g protein	makes 4 muffins each providing 312kcal, 7.3g protein	makes 4 muffins each providing 309kcal, 6.2g protein

Method

1 Preheat oven to moderate 180°C. Place 4 non-stick paper patty cases into a 12-hole (1/3 cup/80ml) muffin pan.

2 Place spinach, egg, sour cream, almond meal, and margarine into a bowl.

3 Blend ingredients using a hand held beater.

4 Add grated cheddar cheese and mix in well.

5 Pour mixture into the patty cases and cook for 20 minutes.

6 Serve each muffin with 1/4 of the cream allowance.

Chocolate cookies

Ingredient:	3:1	3.5:1	4:1
custard powder	42g	30g	30g
chocolate, no added sugar	48g	48g	30g
butter, room temperature	60g	52g	52g
hazelnuts, ground to meal	54g	54g	42g
desiccated coconut	100g	100g	100g
table sugar, white	4g	4g	–
cold water	as needed	as needed	as needed
clotted cream	100g	120g	156g
	makes 12 biscuits each providing 195kcal, 1.6g protein	makes 12 biscuits each providing 196kcal, 1.6g protein	makes 12 biscuits each providing 190kcal, 1.4g protein

Method

1 Preheat oven to moderate (180°C) and lightly grease a biscuit tray with an oil spray.

2 Mix together all of the ingredients.

3 Using heaped teaspoonful quantities, shape mixture into balls. If these do not form easily then add a little extra water to help them combine.

4 Place balls onto the tray and flatten slightly with a fork.

5 Place in the oven and bake for 20 minutes

NB: Liquid artificial sweetener can be added to 4:1 recipe if desired.

Yoyos

Ingredient:	3:1	3.5:1	4:1
self raising flour	24g	24g	24g
butter, room temperature	80g	70g	58g
macadamia nuts, ground to meal	96g	96g	96g
desiccated coconut	48g	48g	48g
table sugar, white	18g	8g	–
water	as needed	as needed	as needed
	makes 10 biscuits each providing 175kcal, 1.3g protein	makes 10 biscuits each providing 164kcal, 1.3g protein	makes 10 biscuits each providing 152kcal, 1.3g protein

Method

1 Pre-heat oven to moderate (180°C). Lightly grease an oven tray with an oil spray.

2 Mix all of the ingredients together.

3 Using heaped teaspoonful quantities, roll mixture into small balls, place on tray and flatten slightly with a fork.

4 Bake in the oven for 20 minutes or until golden on top.

NB: A small amount of water may be needed to hold the mixture together before they are rolled.

MCT ketogenic diet recipes
Breakfast

Porridge

Ingredient:	amount
porridge oats, dry	13g
semi-skimmed milk	50g
double thick cream	20g
Liquigen®	40g
liquid artificial sweetener (optional)	to taste
deli ham, lean	16g
cheddar cheese	12g
semi-skimmed milk	70g

makes 1 serve
providing
410kcal, 12g protein
20g MCT fat, 18g LCT fat
15g carbohydrate

Method

1 Stir the oats into the combined milk and cream.

2 Microwave on high for 2 minutes then add Liquigen® and liquid artificial sweetener (optional). Microwave on high for 1 minute. Stir well and let stand for 1 minute.

3 Serve porridge with ham, cheese and milk to drink.

Scrambled egg on toast

Ingredient:	amount
whole egg, beaten	50g
Liquigen®	40g
butter	12g
salt and pepper	to taste
wholemeal bread	24g
semi-skimmed milk	120g

makes 1 serve
providing
410kcal, 12g protein
20g MCT fat, 18g LCT fat
15g carbohydrate

Method

1 Mix together egg, Liquigen®, and half of the butter.

2 Microwave on high until egg is just set; approximately 50 seconds. Season with salt and pepper.

3 Meanwhile, toast the bread, spread with the remaining butter.

4 Serve toast with the scrambled egg and milk.

Mains

Beef and vegetables with chocolate pudding
photographed next page

Beef and Vegetables	
Ingredient:	amount
MCT oil	40g
olive oil	8g
onion, peeled, finely chopped	40g
mushroom, finely chopped	80g
new potato, boiled, sliced	172g
chicken stock cube	pinch
garlic powder	pinch
salt and pepper	pinch
tomato, canned, diced	80g
boiling water	as needed
beef strips, grilled	80g
cauliflower, boiled	200g
carrot, peeled and boiled	40g

MCT pudding	
Ingredient:	amount
butter, melted	24g
cocoa powder	pinch
double thick cream	40g
Liquigen®	80g
liquid artificial sweetener	to taste
pure vanilla essence	to taste

makes 4 serves
each providing
360kcal, 9g protein
20g MCT fat, 13g LCT fat
11g carbohydrate

Method

Beef and vegetables

1 Place both oils into a large sized non-stick frying pan and heat to medium. Add potato slices and fry until cooked. Set aside.

2 Add onion and mushroom to pan and fry until soft.

3 Add stock cube, garlic powder, salt and pepper, canned tomatoes and boiling water.

4 Serve onion and mushroom sauce with potato, beef, cauliflower and carrot.

MCT pudding

1 Place melted butter and cocoa powder into a small bowl. Mix together.

2 Stir in the cream, Liquigen®, liquid sweetener and vanilla essence.

3 Pour into an ice cube tray and freeze. Makes 12 chocolates, 3 per serve.

Beef and vegetables with chocolate pudding

Chicken and vegetable korma

Chicken and vegetable korma

photographed previous page

Ingredient:	amount
MCT oil	60g
olive oil	8g
chicken breast, sliced	80g
garlic, mild chilli powder, tumeric	pinch of each, to taste
spring onion, sliced	80g
mushroom, sliced	160g
carrot, boiled, sliced	40g
cauliflower, boiled, diced	160g
powdered chicken stock	to taste
liquid artificial sweetener	to taste
lemon or lime juice	to taste
almonds, crushed	36g
double thick cream	40g
Liquigen®	40g
water	as needed

Ingredient:	amount
apple, peeled, sliced, chilled	280g

Method

1 Place both oils into a large non-stick frying pan. Heat to a medium heat. Fry the chicken with the spices, spring onion and mushroom until the chicken is tender.

2 Stir in cauliflower and carrot. Add powdered stock, sweetener, and juice. Stir in almonds, cream, Liquigen® and water.

3 Serve korma hot followed by chilled apple for dessert.

Pizza

Ingredient:	amount
MCT oil	20g
wholemeal bread	18g
mushroom, sliced	40g
zucchini, sliced	20g
tomato, diced, canned	50g
garlic, mixed herbs	to taste
cheddar cheese, grated	15g
salami, finely sliced	7g

cucumber	60g
vinegar, optional	to taste
mayonnaise	6g

makes 1 serve
providing
360kcal, 9g protein
20g MCT fat, 13g LCT fat
11g carbohydrate

Method

1 Place MCT oil into a small non-stick frying pan.

2 Heat to a medium heat and fry one side of the bread until crisp, remove from pan and set aside.

3 Fry mushroom and zucchini in remaining oil until crisp.

4 On the non-fried side, top bread with tomato, garlic, herbs, mushroom and zucchini.

5 Sprinkle grated cheese over the top of the mushroom and zucchini.

6 Place sliced salami on top of the cheese.

7 Place pizza under a pre-heated grill and cook until the cheese has melted.

8 Serve with a side of cucumber, optional vinegar, and mayonnaise.

Baked eggs

Ingredient:	amount
whole egg	50g
double thick cream	8g
Liquigen®	40g
broccoli, steamed	25g
zucchini, steamed	25g
water crackers	10g
butter	4g

makes 1 serve
providing
360kcal, 9g protein
20g MCT fat, 13g LCT fat
11g carbohydrate

Method

1 Pre-heat oven to moderate (180°C). Place 2 non-stick paper patty cases into a 12-hole (⅓ cup/80ml) muffin pan.

2 In a small bowl whisk together the egg, cream and Liquigen®.

3 Stir in the vegetables.

4 Pour mixture evenly between 2 patty cases and cook for approximately 20 minutes.

5 Serve baked eggs with crackers spread with butter.

Picnic time

Ingredient:	amount
carrot, sliced	20g
avocado, mashed	20g
mayonnaise	10g
cream cheese	52g
MCT oil	40g
mixed herbs, pepper	to taste
cucumber, raw, sliced	80g
red pepper, raw, sliced	20g
wholemeal bread	24g
green grapes, seedless	20g
strawberries	80g
deli ham, lean	34g
	makes 2 serves each providing 360kcal, 9g protein 20g MCT fat, 13g LCT fat 11g carbohydrate

Method

1 Mix together the avocado, mayonnaise and cream cheese. Stir in the MCT oil, herbs and pepper.

2 Serve chilled with the carrot, cucumber and pepper. The bread, grapes, strawberries and ham are eaten as part of the meal.

Snacks

Celeriac crisps

Ingredient:	amount
MCT oil	20g
celeriac, sliced	120g
dried herbs, salt and pepper	to taste
cheddar cheese	10g
deli ham, lean	24g
apple, peeled, sliced	154g
	makes 2 serves each providing 160kcal, 4g protein 10g MCT fat, 2g LCT fat 10.5g carbohydrate

Method

1 Heat MCT oil in a small non-stick frying pan to a medium heat.

2 Fry celeriac in MCT oil with herbs and salt and pepper until celeriac has just softened and outside is slightly crunchy.

3 Serve crisps with cheese, ham and apple.

Snack bar

Ingredient:	amount
wheat bran	48g
whole egg, beaten	72g
MCT oil	60g
blueberries	42g
wholemeal flour	60g
liquid artificial sweetener	to taste

makes 6 serves
each providing
160kcal, 4g protein
10g MCT fat, 2g LCT fat
10.5g carbohydrate

Method

1 Pre-heat oven to moderate (180 °C). Line a 19cm x 19cm baking tray with baking paper.

2 In a medium sized bowl mix together the bran, egg, MCT oil, blueberries and flour.

3 Add artificial sweetener to desired taste and stir in thoroughly.

4 Place mixture onto prepared tray and shape into a square.

5 Cook in the oven for 20 minutes. Allow to cool in the tray for 15 minutes to make certain all the oil is absorbed and the slice is moist.

6 Cut into 6 even sized bars and enjoy warm or cooled.

Chocolate brownie

Ingredient:	amount
cocoa powder	18g
whole egg, beaten	72g
Liquigen®	120g
wholemeal flour	96g
liquid artificial sweetener	to taste
	makes 6 serves each providing 160kcal, 4g protein 10g MCT fat, 2g LCT fat 10.5g carbohydrate

Method

1 Pre-heat oven to moderate (180 °C). Lightly grease a 6-hole silicon muffin tray with an oil spray.

2 Mix together all of the ingredients in a medium sized bowl. Divide mixture evenly between the 6 muffin holes.

3 Bake in the oven for 15 minutes. Allow to cool in the tray before serving.

NB: For a more biscuit like texture replace the Liquigen® with 60g MCT oil.

MCT cooking tips

Many parents struggle to hide MCT oil and Liquigen® in meals and snacks. Not many children are happy to drink either alongside their meals. The following are some ideas to help parents hide these MCT fats.

1 Liquigen® and MCT oil are interchangeable: 50g Liquigen® = 25g MCT oil

2 Try mixing Liquigen® with diet soft drink. Some children like this combination as it is, others like this combination mixed with semi skimmed milk and double thick cream.

3 Liquigen® "Ice-cream" using the above ingredients, or use the above ingredients without the diet soft drink. Instead use cocoa powder, coffee powder or sugar free syrups to flavour the ice-cream.

4 Without freezing, the above suggestions become Liquigen® "milkshakes".

5 Liquigen® mixes very well into egg. As well as omelettes, scrambled eggs and frittatas, try making pancakes. Use a little flour, egg, cream or milk, and Liquigen® to make a batter and then fry. These taste great served with lemon juice and sweetener or low carbohydrate fruit such as blueberries.

6 Add Liquigen® to low sugar yoghurts such as Muller® light. These can be eaten as they are or frozen. Liquigen® can also be added to sugar free jelly.

7 In the cooler weather, try adding Liquigen® to soup. It is best to heat the soup and add the Liquigen® at the end. Heated Liquigen® has a distinctive smell that many children dislike.

8 Liquigen® and MCT oil can be used for making sauces. Cheese sauces work particularly well. Try mixing them with different cheeses such as cream, stilton or cheddar. Sauces can then be stirred into a meal or served on the side.

9 MCT oil mixes in well to Alpro® soya desserts; the dark chocolate flavour is particularly tasty and freezes well with the MCT oil mixed through. The vanilla flavour version works well in place of custard on fruit such as rhubarb; MCT oil and sweetener can then be mixed through this combination.

10 An easy sauce for pasta can be made by using MCT oil, grated cheese and double thick cream. Simply combine these ingredients and heat in the microwave. Once heated they can be used on your child's favourite pasta, salmon and more…

11   MCT oil fried with chopped onion, garlic, pepper, cream or stilton cheese makes a yummy sauce for steak or fish.

12   MCT oil fried with chopped onion and mushroom, a little garlic and tomato, a pinch of OXO® and herbs, makes a delicious gravy for roast dinners.

13   In the warmer months, MCT oil can be used to make salad dressing. Simply mix together MCT oil, vinegar, garlic and herbs and pour over salad leaves.

14   MCT oil can also be used to make desserts. Try baking banana and MCT oil in the oven. Bake at a low temperature until browned. Serve with cream.

Directory of ingredients

Spices

The following 'marriages', as they are called in 'chef world', will add further flavour to the ketogenic diet meals. You do need to be careful using fresh herbs because of their carbohydrate content, and although a pinch of dried herbs/spices in your cooking should not cause problems, always check with your dietician.

Basil: tastes great in tomato and pasta dishes but it is also good for roasted chicken, lamb, or fish. It blends well with garlic, thyme, and oregano.

Cayenne Pepper: Try adding cayenne pepper to salsa or avocado dip. Spice up your vegetable dips and dressings with a pinch of cayenne pepper. You can make an omelette with tomatoes, onions, peppers, and a pinch of cayenne pepper added to the egg.

Coriander: Ground coriander seed is always good in curries, meat, and seafood dishes.

Garlic: Can add fantastic flavour. Use a pinch of minced garlic in pasta sauces, stews, and soups. Mix with oil and vinegar and Italian spices to make salad dressing. Garlic powder can be used in marinades, or mixed with herbs and rubbed into poultry, pork, or beef before cooking.

Oregano: Tastes great with tomato, egg, or cheese based foods, and is also a great addition to many lamb, pork, and beef main dishes. Try sautéing vegetables in olive oil with garlic and oregano. You can make a savoury sauce with melted butter, lemon juice and a bit of oregano; drizzle it over grilled fish and poultry. A pinch of dried oregano leaves is also an easy way to accent pasta sauces, salad dressings and ground meat dishes.

Paprika: Is useful as a simple garnish for almost any savoury dish. Combine it with butter, margarine, or oil for a quick baste for fish or poultry. This is especially good on roast turkey.

Sage: Use ground sage sparingly; foods absorb its flavour more quickly than leaf sage. Top swordfish, tuna, steaks, chicken, and turkey pieces with sage & lemon butter. Rub sage, cracked pepper, and garlic into pork tenderloin or chops before cooking.

Tarragon: This adds flavour to egg and cheese dishes, soups and fresh fruits. To baste chicken, fish or seafood, blend tarragon with butter, chives, and lemon.

Thyme: Rub minced garlic and thyme over lamb, pork, or beef roasts. Season cheese, tomato, and egg dishes with thyme.

Australian brands

Cheese
Mainland Cheddar Masters®
Tasmanian Heritage®
Triple Cream Brie Mil El® Parmesan

Chocolate
Well Naturally®
Sweet William®

Cream
double thick: Gippsland Coles®
King Island Dairy®
clotted: Wattle Valley®

Ice-cream
Peters® no added sugar vanilla ice-cream

Margarine
Tablelands®
dairy free: Nuttlex®
Becel®

Mayonnaise
Thomy®
Praise® whole egg

Nut meals
Duck®
Lucky®

Nut spread
Macadamia Melrose® spread
peanut butter: Kraft® nuts smooth

Oils
Alfa One® rice bran oil

Pasta
Casa Barelli® fresh egg fettuccine

Pesto
Sacla® classic pesto

Sauces
Heinz® big red lite

Seed paste
Pureharvest®

Sweeteners
Sucaryl®
Sugarless®

.

United Kingdom brands

Cheese
Boursin®
Philadelphia®
Babybel®

Cocoa Powder
Cadbury Bournville® cocoa powder

Flavourings
Da Vinci® sugar free syrup
Crusha® no added sugar

Margarine/butter
Country life British®
Pure® dairy free

Mayonnaise
Hellmans® full fat

Oils
Alfa One® rice bran oil
Morrisons®

Peanut Butter
Whole Earth® no added sugar

Sausages
Black Farmer® low carbohydrate
Morrisons® frankfurters

Snacks/Desserts
Hartleys® sugar free jelly
Hartleys® sugar free ice pops
Alpro® soya desserts
Alpro ® plain yoghurt
Muller® light yoghurts
Yeo Valley® full fat yoghurt

Spreads and Gravy
Marmite®
Bovril®
Knorr® touch of taste beef or chicken
Oxo®
Tesco® stock

Sweeteners
Hermesetas® liquid or tablets

Useful resources

Websites

http://www.matthewsfriends.org
A website written by Matthew's Friends, an organisation that has grown from parents of children on the diet, to support carers in the management of the ketogenic diet. It also aims to provide the latest ketogenic diet information and ketogenic dietary services in the UK, and further afield, for children and adults.

www.charliefoundation.org
An American organisation that provides support and information for families using the ketogenic diet. The website offers further information and a range of resources.

http://www.rch.org.au
Website outlining the ketogenic diet program at the Royal Children's Hospital, Melbourne, Australia with answers to some frequently asked questions.

http://www.shsweb.co.uk
Information on Ketocal®, a nutritionally complete powdered ketogenic diet formula, produced by Nutricia.

Books

Freeman JM, Kossoff EH, Freeman JB, Kelly MT. The Ketogenic Diet: A Treatment for Children and Others with Epilepsy. 4th Edition. Demos Medical Publishing. 2007.

Kossoff EH, Freeman J, Turner Z, Rubenstein J. Ketogenic Diets: Treatments for Epilepsy and Other Disorders. 5th Edition. Demos Medical Publishing. 2011.

Ketogenic diet computer programs/ Ketogenic diet calculators

United Kingdom uses EKM2000. For details go to:
http://www.edm2000.com

An Australian excel computer program can be obtained by contacting the Children's Epilepsy Program at the Royal Children's Hospital, Melbourne:
www.rch.org.au/cep

Index

Acknowledgments

The authors would like to thank paediatric dietitian Elizabeth Neal for her help with the MCT section, celebrity chef Tony Tobin for his support and contribution particularly to the spice section, senior ketogenic assistant at Matthew's Friends, Val Aldridge, and Natalie Bryant for considerable assistance with formatting and proofreading of the book. We would also like to thank Matthew's Friends, the UK organization supporting dietary treatments for epilepsy and Jeannette Irons for their donation, and Nutricia and Vitaflo for their financial contribution to the development of this book.

The authors are indebted to Greg Elms, one of Australia's leading food photographers. Greg has been shooting professionally for 20 years, winning numerous awards, including USA's Cordon D'Or Award in 2006 and 2007, and contributing to many books and magazines. His skill in depicting the ketogenic diet meals has made them look truly delectable!